Oxford University Press,
Great Clarendon Street,
Oxford OX2 6DP

Oxford New York
Athens Auckland Bangkok Bogota Bombay
Buenos Aires Calcutta Cape Town Dar es Salaam
Delhi Florence Hong Kong Istanbul Karachi
Kuala Lumpur Madras Madrid Melbourne
Mexico City Nairobi Paris Singapore
Taipei Tokyo Toronto Warsaw

and associated companies in
Berlin Ibadan

Oxford is a trade mark of Oxford University Press

ISBN 0 19 913380 8 School Edition
First published 1996
Reprinted 1997 (three times)
ISBN 0 19 913377 8 Bookshop Edition
First published 1996
Reprinted 1997 (three times)

Typesetting, artwork, and design by Ian Foulis & Associates,
Saltash, Cornwall.

Printed by Canale, Italy

Acknowledgements

The publisher and authors would like to thank the following for
their permission to reproduce photographs and other copyright
material:

p 6 Ace/Mugshots/G Palmer (left), Allsport (right), p 7 Allsport,
p 9 Colorsport (left), Allsport (right), p 11 Sporting Pictures,
p 14 Science Photo Library/NASA (right), p 17 SPL/J Stevenson
(all), p 18 SPL/J Stevenson, p 19 SPL/M Kage, p 20 Bubbles/
I West, p 21 SPL/ A Tsiaris, p 25 Allsport (all), p 28 SPL/M
Kage, SPL/Prof Motta E Vizza, p 31 Allsport (left), Colorsport
(right), p 41 Allsport, p 42 SPL/J Revy, p 45 Micro Medical (top
left & right), Allsport (bottom), p 50 SPL/ J Radcliffe Hospital,
p 51 SPL, p 52 SPL/BSIP, LBL, p 53 SPL/Dr Marazzi (top
right), SPL/Dr H Robinson (bottom right), p 54 SPL/J Selby, p 55
SPL/S Terry, p 57 Colorsport, p 59 Allsport, p 63 Allsport (all),
p 65 Allsport (top), Colorsport (bottom), p 67 Allsport (all), p 69
Colorsport, p 76 Action Images, p 77 Allsport (left), SPL/L
Mulvehill (right), p 78 Colorsport, p 81 Allsport,
p 83 Physio-med, p 84 Allsport (all), p 97 Action Images,
pp 88 & 89 Colorsport, p 102 SPL/Prof P Motta, pp 105 & 106
Colorsport, p 109 SPL/J Stevenson, p 110 SPL/ Eye of Science
(top right), Allsport (left), p 111 SPL/Dr P Marazzi (all), p 114
Allsport, p 115 Action Images (all), p 117 Action Plus, p 121
Action Images (left), Colorsport (right), p 124 Allsport, p 127
D Cooper/Photostage (left), p 127 Allsport (right), p 128
Allsport, p 129 J Allan Cash, pp 132 & 133 Action Images, p 136
SHOUT, p 138 SPL, p 142 Colorsport, p 142 J Allan Cash, pp
143, 147, 149, 151 Action Images, p 152 Allsport, pp 156 & 157
R Price, 158 Colorsport, p 165 Popperfoto, p 165 J Allan Cash,
p 169 Allsport, p 170 Popperfoto, p 172 Allsport, p 173
Popperfoto, p 177 Colorsport, pp 177 & 178 Action Images,
pp 179, 180, 181 Colorsport, p 182 Bubbles/J Farrow (top),
Ace/R Howard (bottom), p 185 Allsport (top), Sporting Pictures
(bottom), p 186 Colorsport, p 187 Action Plus.

Logos courtesy of organizations concerned.

Cartoons p. 34 Steve Evans.

Special thanks to Astor School, Dover.

Additional photography by Martin Sookias.

Front cover photograph by Tony Stone Images.

Every effort has been made to trace and contact copyright holders
of material reproduced in this book. Any omissions will be
rectified in subsequent printings if notice is given to the publisher.

Thanks are due to Ray Kershaw for his help in obtaining
statistics, the Office for National Statistics for providing
information on levels of participation in physical recreation, and
Bernard Lee for his help with the physiology content.

The authors would like to thank Victoria Powell for her help in
preparing the typescript and Jem Nicholls for his constructive
criticism and advice.

The authors would also like to thank RoseMarie Gallagher for her
help in writing this book.

PE to 16

Sally Fountain and **Linda Gee**

OXFORD UNIVERSITY PRESS

Introduction

PE is an exciting subject. You'll discover how your body works, and how you get and stay fit. You'll find out how you 'learn' a sport, and the things that affect how well you play it. You'll also take a broader look at sport: how it is organized, and the issues that surround it in our society.

The aim of this book is to make your study of PE easy and enjoyable. Look at the contents list. You will see that each chapter is divided into topics. Each topic is just two pages long.

At the end of each topic there's a set of questions. These will help you check that you have understood the topic. At the end of each chapter you'll find a longer set of questions. These will be useful in helping you prepare for your exam.

But remember, what you learn in PE class is not just for an exam. It is also to help you stay fit and healthy, and get as much as you can out of life.

Contents

Section 3 Sport and you

Section 4 Sport in society

1.1 Health and fitness

You have no colds, flu, aches or pains, and you can run a mile in six minutes. But does that mean you are healthy and fit?

What is health?

Health doesn't just mean the absence of sickness.
Health is a state of complete physical, mental and social well-being.
It means you feel good all round.

Physical well-being   Physical well-being means:

- your heart, lungs and other body systems are working well.
- you have no illnesses or injuries.

Mental well-being   Mental well-being means:

- you are able to cope with stress. For example when you run into problems, or have to work very hard before exams.
- you are able to control your emotions. Even if you feel very angry you don't get violent.
- you feel positive about yourself. You know you are okay as a person. You have **self-esteem**.

Social well-being   Social well-being means:

- you have enough to eat, and clothing and shelter. These are the most basic human needs.
- you have friendship and support.
- you feel you have some value in society, whether it is in school, in a job or in your family.

These kinds of well-being are all related. If you get injured in a car accident it may affect your mental well-being. It may also affect your social well-being, if you can't work and lose touch with your friends.

Having fun with your friends is part of a healthy lifestyle. But are you as fit as a top-class athlete? Do you need to be? Could you be?

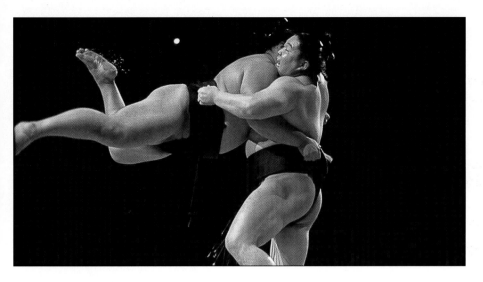

For a sumo wrestler life makes some pretty hefty demands!

What is fitness?

Fitness isn't just being able to do sit-ups or run fast.
Fitness is the ability to meet the demands of the environment.

Your environment is everything around you. It includes home, school, family and friends. All of them make demands on you. Meeting the demands means carrying out tasks and activities. For example:

> cycling to and from school every day
> concentrating on lessons all day
> doing two hours of school work every evening
> helping at home with shopping and cleaning
> playing for the team twice a week
> working in the supermarket on Saturday
> going out with friends at the weekend to a party or the club.

If you can carry out these tasks and activities *without getting too tired*, and still have energy left over for emergencies, then you are fit.

The link between health and fitness

Health and fitness are closely linked. The more easily you can meet the demands on you, the less likely you are to suffer stress, or fall ill, or injure yourself. But if you are ill, you won't be able to meet those demands. You may have to stay off school, give up your Saturday job, and stay in bed for a week or two.

Exercise makes you healthier. It also makes you fitter. You can find out more about this in the next Unit.

Questions

1 What is *health*?
2 Give two examples of mental well-being.
3 What is *physical well-being*?
4 Give two examples of social well-being.

5 What is: a fitness? b your environment?
6 'Being fit' is different for you and for an Olympic sprinter. Explain why.
7 Is there a link between health and fitness? Explain.

1.2 Why exercise?

There are many ways to take exercise. Walking, swimming, aerobics, rugby, golf and judo are just some of them. What can exercise do for you? Lots, as you'll see below.

Physical benefits

Exercise helps you to look good and feel good.

- It burns up stored body fat, so your shape improves and you won't be overweight.
- It tones up the muscles of your back and abdomen, so your posture improves.
- It strengthens your bones.
- It keeps your joints flexible, so you can move efficiently.
- It makes your heart and lungs work more efficiently, so you don't get tired so easily.
- It helps to prevent heart disease, high blood pressure, back pain and cancers. Swimming and walking help people with asthma.

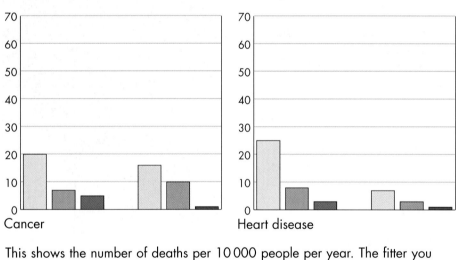

This shows the number of deaths per 10 000 people per year. The fitter you are, the lower your risk of heart disease and cancer. Exercise is the way to improve your fitness.

Mental benefits

Exercise helps your mental well-being too.

- It is stimulating and enjoyable. It peps you up.
- It relieves tension and stress, which can cause high blood pressure and heart disease. A lively game or work out helps you get rid of the tensions from a difficult day.
- It gets rid of aggression. You can take out angry feelings on a ball or bike pedals instead of a person.
- It helps you forget your problems. When you think about them later, they won't seem so bad.
- It relieves boredom and provides a challenge.
- It helps you sleep better, so you feel more rested.
- If you look and feel better, your self-confidence increases.
- Success at a sport is good for your self-esteem.

Even *watching* sport can provide plenty of benefits. Can you name some?

Social well-being

Exercise increases your social well-being, and especially if it's in the form of a sport.

- Exercise helps to make you confident. That means you can cope better with difficult people and difficult situations.
- Playing sport is a way to meet people and make good friends.
- Sport develops teamwork and co-operation. These qualities will help you in your working life.
- You may find you are talented at a sport. You may be able to make a career of it.
- You can choose a sport that suits your personality and makes you feel fulfilled. For example rock climbing might suit if you like to get away from it all and enjoy a challenge.

Exercise and fitness

All those benefits means that exercise helps you meet the demands of your environment more easily. In other words it makes you fitter. You can work harder, feel less tired and enjoy life more. The way to improve your fitness is through exercise.

Brough Scott, former jockey, now a TV commentator. But an interest in sport can lead to a career even if you're not a top-class performer.

Questions

1 Give two examples of how:
   a exercise helps you look better
   b exercise helps your body work better
   c exercise helps to keep disease at bay.
2 Give three mental benefits of exercise.

3 Playing a sport can improve your social well-being. Write down four ways it can do this.
4 Many people earn a living from sport and exercise. Sports journalists and aerobics teachers are examples. Write down as many others as you can.

1.3 Exercise and the body systems

A car has an ignition system, a brake system, a cooling system and so on. Your body also has different systems. They work together to make the body a truly brilliant machine.

When you run, it's not just a case of moving your arms and legs. All your **body systems** work together.

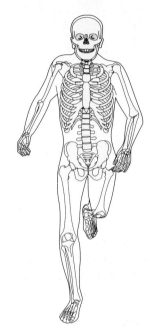

Your **skeletal system**. It's your bones and joints. Without bones you'd be a shapeless heap. Your joints allow movement.

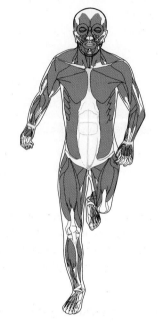

Your **muscular system**. Muscles are the red meat around bones. They pull on bones and make them move.

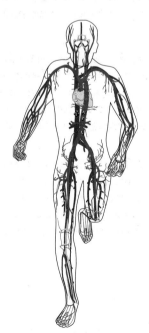

Your **circulatory system**: blood, heart and blood vessels. Blood carries food and oxygen round the body and carries waste away.

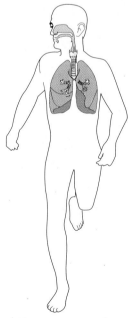

Your **respiratory system**: the lungs and breathing tube. It's how you take in oxygen and get rid of carbon dioxide.

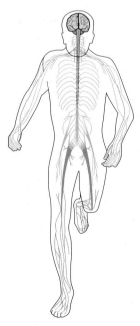

Your **nervous system**: the brain, spinal cord and a network of nerves. It controls and co-ordinates movement.

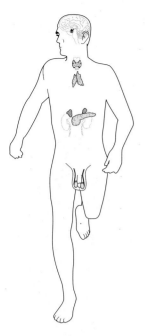

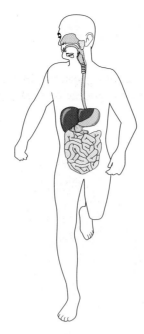

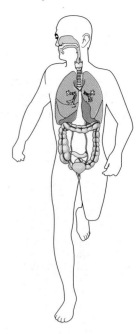

Your **hormonal system**: a set of glands which make **hormones**. These chemicals help to control activities going on in your body.

Your **digestive system**: the stomach and gut, where the food you eat gets broken down. You use digested food as fuel.

Your **excretory system**: the lungs, kidneys and intestine. They get rid of or **excrete** the waste from your body.

How body systems work together: an example

Warming up for an important game? This shows how body systems work together:

1 Signals from the eyes, ears, muscles and skin tell your brain you're on the way. It responds by sending signals around your body along the nervous system.

2 At a signal, a gland pumps **adrenaline** into your blood. This hormone makes your heart and lungs work faster and gets your muscles ready for action.

3 Your heart pumps blood to your muscles. It brings food, oxygen and adrenaline. It carries carbon dioxide away.

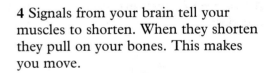

4 Signals from your brain tell your muscles to shorten. When they shorten they pull on your bones. This makes you move.

5 Food from your digestive system is stored as **body fat** and as **glycogen** in muscles. Your muscles use these as fuel to get energy for movement.

6 The lungs take in oxygen, which you also need for energy. They excrete carbon dioxide, a waste material, at the same time.

Questions

1 List eight systems that act together to keep your body going. Say what each does.

2 What does *excrete* mean?

3 What is *adrenaline*? What does it do?

4 Look at note 4 for the photograph above. It shows the nervous and muscular systems at work together. For each of the other notes say which system or systems are at work.

Questions on Chapter 1

1 What is health?

2 Match each statement below to the letter A, B or C.
You might want to choose more than one letter for some.
A physical well-being
B mental well-being
C social well-being

  a You get on well with your friends and they help you in times of trouble.
  b Your blood pressure is normal.
  c You have a job, and it pays pretty well.
  d You play in a football team and really enjoy it.
  e When something upsets you, you think it over but you don't let it get you down.
  f You haven't had an infection for years.
  g You have high self-esteem.

3 Match each statement below to the letter A, B or C.
You might want to choose more than one letter for some.
A physical well-being
B mental well-being
C social well-being

  a depression
  b a broken leg
  c homelessness
  d tension at work
  e hardening of the arteries
  f divorce
  g fear of crossing the street

4 People sometimes get so depressed they can't work.
They don't go out. They don't eat properly so they get run down and fall ill. Their physical, mental and social well-being all suffer.
Make up an example of your own, to show how the three aspects of health affect each other.

5 a What is fitness?
  b A county tennis player and an international tennis player both need to be fit. But the international player needs a higher level of fitness. Do you agree? Explain your answer.

6 The physical demands on each of these are different.
Arrange them in order with the least demands first.

  a member of the England rowing team
  a bus conductor
  an office worker who sits at a desk all day
  an under-sixteen county football player
  a seventy-year-old bedridden person
  an Olympic triathlon champion

7 a List all the reasons why exercise is good for you.
     (Try to do this without looking back in the chapter.)
  b Now put these reasons in order of importance to *you*.

8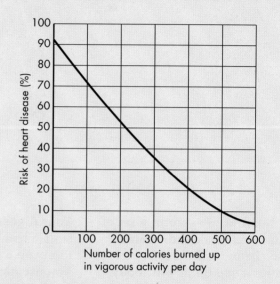

This graph shows how the average risk of heart disease changes with exercise, for the population in general.

A 100% risk means you are certain to get some form of heart disease. It does *not* mean you will die from it!
An 80% risk means heart disease is very likely.

  a What is the maximum risk of heart disease for someone who does no vigorous exercise?
  b You burn up about 100 calories of energy when you walk a mile at a brisk pace.
     What is the risk of heart disease if you do this every day? By how much has it fallen from the maximum?
  c You burn up about 10 calories a minute when you run moderately fast. About how much would you burn up a 30-minute run?
  d What is the risk of heart disease if you do this every day? By how much has it fallen from the maximum?
  e What conclusion can you draw about exercise as a protection against heart disease?

9 Say whether the statement is true or false.
  a Gardening and cleaning are forms of exercise.
  b It is not possible for a seventy-year-old to be fit.
  c There is no connection between fitness and health.
  d Environment just means the air around you.
  e Exercise improves your fitness.
  f The fitter you are, the more demands you can meet.
  g If your normal activities make you feel worn out, that means you are unfit.

10 See if you can answer without looking back at the chapter. For each body system, say:
  i   what it is called
  ii what it is made up of
  iii what its job is.

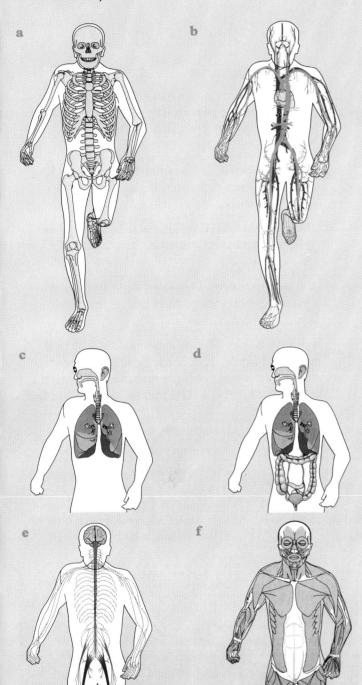

a

b

c

d

e

f

11 You will not find the answers to this question in the chapter. See how much you can answer without help from your teacher. There may be more than one answer to each part.

Look again at the body systems in question 10. Say which you think is affected by:
  i   smoking
  ii   poor diet
  iii   lack of calcium
  iv   being overweight
  v   lack of iron
  vi   family quarrels
  vii   too many late nights
  viii measles
  ix   homelessness
  x   alcohol
  xi   drug abuse
  xii   a broken leg in a skiing accident

12 Look again at the body systems in question 10. Which do you think are affected by exercise?

13 Write down two examples to show how fitness can be affected by:
  a poor eyesight
  b poor hearing

14 Your physical surroundings, and what you eat, affect your health and therefore your fitness. Think of one example where people's health has been affected by:
  a air pollution
  b water pollution
  c noise
  d sunshine
  e infected food

15 Smoking affects your health and fitness. This shows figures from research carried out some years ago.

	Death from lung cancer per 100 000 people
non-smokers	7
light smokers	47
moderate smokers	86
heavy smokers	166

What can you say about the relationship between smoking and lung cancer?

16 a In the year 1991 - 92, 53 million working days were lost due to heart disease. The government paid on average £8 sickness benefit a day to each sick person. How much did heart disease cost the government in terms of sickness benefit that year?
  b Imagine you are the Minister for Health. Try to think of five things you would do to make the population of the UK more healthy.

13

2.1 Bones

How tall will you be? It depends on how fast your bones are growing. They don't stop completely until you are in your early twenties.

A typical adult long bone

The arm and leg bones of an adult look like this:

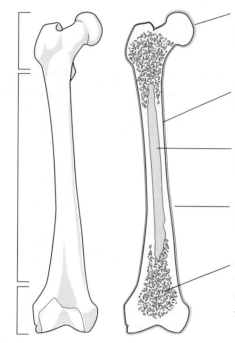

the end part is called the **epiphysis**

the long shaft is called the **diaphysis**

epiphysis

cartilage. This is smooth and slippery, a bit like thick white plastic. It protects the ends of the bone where it meets other bones.

compact bone. This is hard and strong. It is made of fibres cemented with calcium salts.

the **marrow cavity**. This is filled with a soft yellow pulp called marrow.

the **periosteum**. This is a tough fibrous skin that covers all except the ends of the bone.

spongy bone. This is also made of calcium salts and fibres. It is hard, light and very strong. In some spongy bone the holes are filled with red marrow, which makes blood cells.

Bone cells

Even when a bone has stopped growing, it is full of life.
Bone cells called **osteoblasts** keep making new bone. At the same time other bone cells called **osteoclasts** break it down.
When you exercise, you put pressure on your bones. This makes the osteoblasts work harder and helps to keep your bones strong.

Press-ups get those osteoblasts going! But in space, weightlessness means both bones and muscles will weaken. So an exercise machine is part of the astronaut's space kit.

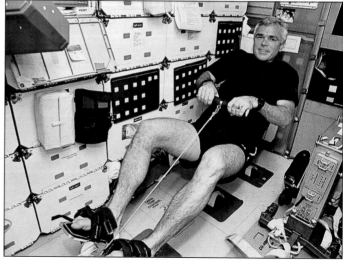

How bones grow

Inside the womb, your bones start life as **cartilage**.
Over the years this turns into bone in a process called **ossification**.
This shows what happens:

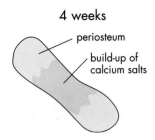

4 weeks

periosteum

build-up of calcium salts

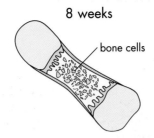

8 weeks

bone cells

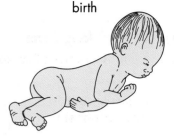

birth

A periosteum grows round the cartilage. It will control the shape and thickness of the bone. Then calcium salts build up.

Bone cells appear in the middle. They start changing the cartilage into bone. The periosteum also lays down bone.

By the time you are born, bones are still mostly cartilage. They are quite soft and easily bent.

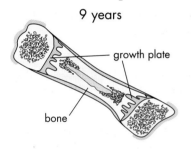

9 years

growth plate

bone

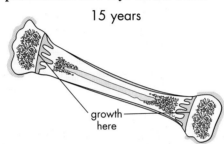

15 years

growth here

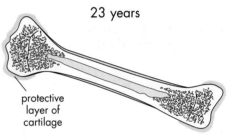

23 years

protective layer of cartilage

Next, bone cells appear at the ends and change these to bone. Two bands of cartilage remain. They are called **growth plates**.

The plates grow at the outer edge. So the bone gets longer. But at the same time the inner edge is being turned into bone.

Growth stops when the plates are all bone. Now the only cartilage left in the bone is the thin layer at each end.

The whole process is controlled by hormones. If there is too much **growth hormone**, the cartilage in the plates grows too fast and the person ends up a giant. If there is too little the person fails to grow.

Bones and ageing

Men's bones are bigger and heavier than women's. But all bones get lighter as people get older, because the osteoblasts don't work so hard. Many older women suffer from **osteoporosis**, where bones get so weak they break easily.

But exercise keeps those osteoblasts working. So it is important to exercise even when you get old.

Questions

1 Draw an adult long bone, and label the parts.
2 What job does this do in the long bone?
 a cartilage **b** red marrow
 c the periosteum
3 Which parts of a bone does the periosteum not cover?
4 Explain why press-ups strengthen arm bones.

5 Why you need calcium in your diet? Where can you get it?
6 What are growth plates? Where are they? Do you have any?
7 At what point do bones stop growing?
8 What is ossification?

2.2 The skeleton

Without your skeleton you'd be just a shapeless sack of flesh.

The skeleton has 206 bones, held together at **joints** by strong fibres called **ligaments**. These are its main bones:

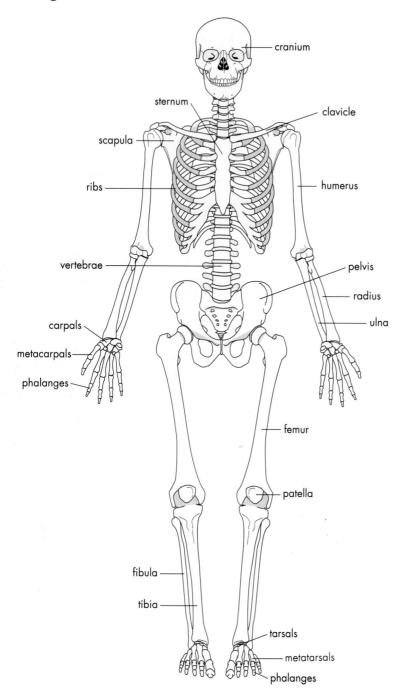

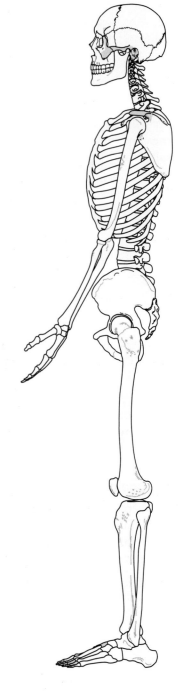

Each arm and leg has three long bones. Look at the bone sticking out at the end of the backbone, in the side view. It's the remains of a tail!

The skeleton shown here is female. Male and female skeletons differ in some ways. For example the male skeleton is usually larger. The female skeleton has a wider pelvis to make it easier to have children.

The functions of the skeleton

1 **Support**. It forms a framework to support your body and give it shape. Just like the steel girders in a building!

2 **Protection**. Some parts of your body are delicate and easily damaged. The skeleton protects them. Your cranium protects your brain. Your ribs and sternum protect your heart and lungs.

3 **Movement**. Your muscles are firmly attached to your skeleton. Muscles work by **contracting** or getting shorter. When they contract they pull on bones. This makes the bones move.

4 **Blood production**. Some bones contain *red* bone marrow. This makes red cells, white cells and platelets for blood. The ribs, vertebrae, humerus and femur all have some red bone marrow.

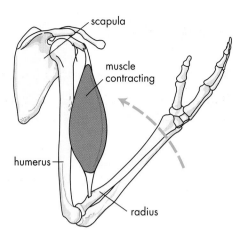

Bones move when muscles contract.

The four types of bones in your skeleton

Your bones are different shapes and sizes because they have different jobs to do. They are divided into four groups:

1 **Long bones**. These are shaped like the bone on page 14. They have a diaphysis, epiphyses and a hollow centre. Your height, shoe size and glove size depend on long bones.

Examples: the bones of the upper and lower arms and legs, the collar bone, the ribs, the metatarsals, metacarpals and phalanges.

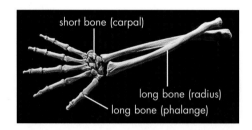

2 **Short bones**. These are small and squat. They are spongy bone covered with a thin layer of compact bone. So they are light and very strong.

Examples: the carpals of the wrist, the tarsals of the feet.

3 **Flat bones**. These are spongy bone between two layers of compact bone. They have a large surface area.

Examples: the scapula, pelvis and cranium.
The scapula and pelvis need a large area for all the muscles that attach to them. The cranium needs a large area to protect the brain.

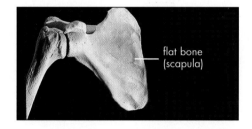

4 **Irregular bones.** These are spongy bone inside and compact bone outside. They are specially shaped to suit the job they have to do.

Examples: the patella, the vertebrae.

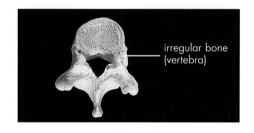

Questions

1 Write these bones in a list. Then write their scientific names beside them:
collar bone   breast bone   backbone
shoulder blade   thigh bone   knee cap
2 The skeleton has four functions. What are they?
3 Give two examples of how the skeleton protects.
4 Give two examples of flat bones, and say why they need a large surface area.
5 Name one long bone that has a big effect on your height.

2.3 A closer look at the skeleton

The vertebral column

Down the back of your skeleton is the backbone or **vertebral column**. It has several different jobs to do.

- It must be able to bend and twist. So it is made up of 34 small bones instead of one long one. They are called **vertebrae**. Most can move a little. Between them they make the backbone very flexible.
- It must be strong, to support your body parts. So it is **curved**. Curved structures are stronger than straight ones. (Think of the arches of bridges.)
- It must protect the **spinal cord**, the bundles of nerves running down from your brain. So the vertebrae have a hole for the spinal cord.

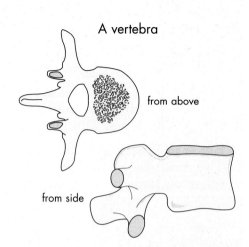

A vertebra

from above

from side

The parts of the vertebral column

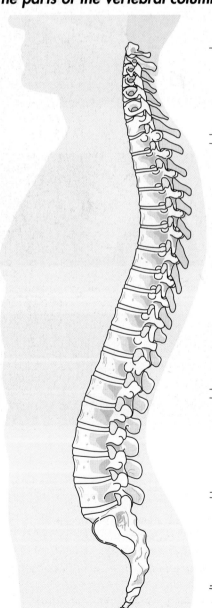

The vertebrae are divided into five groups, each with a different job.

The **cervical vertebrae** (7). These support the neck and head. They allow the most movement, letting you bend and tilt your head and look over your shoulder.

The **thoracic vertebrae** (12). Your ribs are connected to these. They don't move much, so your heart and lungs won't get squashed.

The **lumbar vertebrae** (5). These are big, to support the rest. They allow plenty of twisting and turning. Powerful back muscles attach to the wings at each side.

The **sacrum** (5 fused vertebrae). These form one bone which is then fused to the pelvic girdle. This makes a solid base for the trunk and legs.

The **coccyx** (5 fused vertebrae). Our ancestors had tails, and this part got left behind!

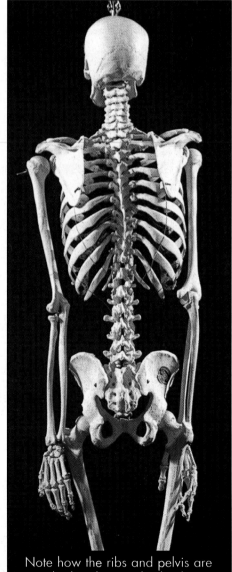

Note how the ribs and pelvis are attached to the vertebral column.

Other bones of the skeleton

The cranium, face bones and ear bones form the **skull**.

The **cranium** or brain case is made of 8 flat bones.
The lower jaw bone or **mandible** is hinged to it so you can chew.

The scapulas (shoulder blades) and clavicles (collar bones) form the **shoulder girdle**. This connects your arms to the centre part of your skeleton.

The top two vertebrae. The skull balances on the **atlas**. The atlas fits over a peg on the **axis** and can rotate on it. So you can turn your head.

You have twelve pairs of **ribs**. All are joined to your vertebrae at the back. Ten pairs are joined to your sternum at the front.

The vetebral column has 26 moving parts.

The bottom two pairs are called **floating ribs**. Can you see why?

The **radius** lines up with your thumb.

The **radius** and **ulna** can partly rotate around each other. This lets you turn your palm up or down. Try it and see!

The pelvis and sacrum form the **pelvic girdle**. This connects your legs to the centre part of your skeleton.

The **patella** or knee cap is not attached to any other bone. It is embedded in the tendon of a muscle. It protects the knee joint.

Questions

1 Think of an example of a sport where it is very helpful that:
   a your backbone has 26 moving parts
   b your backbone is curved
   c your sacrum is fused to your pelvis
   d your cervical vertebrae can move quite a lot.

2 Sketch the vertebral column and label its parts.
3 Which bone is the atlas? What does it do?
4 How many pairs of ribs do you have?
5 Why are the two lowest pairs of ribs called floating ribs?
6 Why are you able to turn your palm up *and* down?

2.4 Different kinds of joints

Your skeleton is made up of bones. **Joints** are where the bones meet. They are divided into three types depending on how freely the bones can move.

Fixed or immoveable joints

The bones at an immoveable joint can't move at all. They interlock or overlap, and are held close together by tough fibre. The joints between the plates in the cranium are a good example.

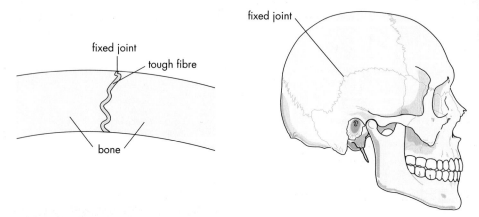

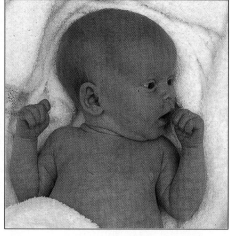

Gaps called **fontanelles** between plates in the cranium allow a baby's head to squash during birth. Twelve months later the gaps will have closed and fixed joints will have started to form.

The fused joints in the sacrum are another example.

Slightly moveable joints

The bones at a slightly moveable joint can move only a little.

They are held together by strong white cords or straps called **ligaments** and joined by **cartilage**. This is like a gristly cushion. It stops the bones from knocking together. It can squash a little to let them move.

The joints between most of your vertebrae are slightly moveable. The pads of cartilage between them act as shock absorbers so the bones won't jar when you run and jump.

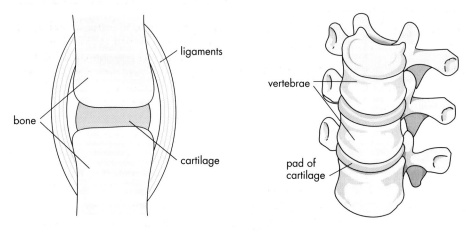

The joints between your ribs and sternum are also slightly moveable. They move a little when you breathe in and out.

Freely moveable joints

At a freely moveable joint the bones can move quite freely. The knee joint is a good example.

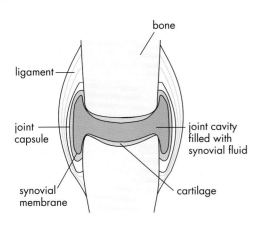

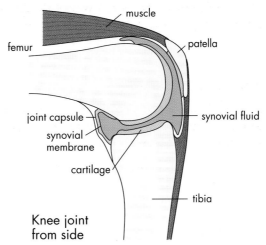

Knee joint from side

A freely moveable joint has these parts:

- an outer sleeve called the **joint capsule**. This holds the bones together and protects the joint. It is an extension of the skin or periosteum that covers each bone.
- a **synovial membrane**. This lines the capsule and oozes a slippery liquid called **synovial fluid**.
- a **joint cavity**. This is the small gap between the bones. It is filled with synovial fluid. This lubricates the joint so that the bones can move more easily.
- a covering of smooth slippery **cartilage** on the ends of the bones. It stops the bones knocking together.
- **ligaments** which hold the bones together and keep them in place.

Freely moveable joints are also called **synovial joints**. (Why?)
Most of your joints are synovial. Otherwise you couldn't move so easily!
The elbow, shoulder, hip and finger joints are examples.

Cartilage and ligaments: a reminder

Cartilage protects bones and stops them knocking together.
It forms a gristly cushion between the bones at slightly moveable joints.
It forms a smooth slippery coat on the ends of bones at synovial joints.

Ligaments are the strong cords and straps that lash bones together and hold a joint in place. They are just a bit elastic - enough to let the bones move. (If bones moved too much they would tear your flesh.)

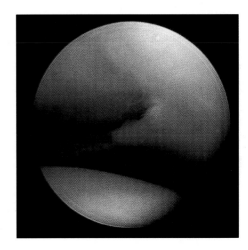

Damaged knee cartilage, filmed using a tiny camera attached to a tiny scalpel, inserted into the knee joint through a small cut. The surgeon can shave and reshape the damaged cartilage by remote control.

Questions

1 What is a *joint*?
2 Describe: **a** a fixed joint **b** a slightly moveable joint. Give two examples of each.
3 Which type of joint is the most common in your body? Give four examples.

4 **a** Draw and label a synovial joint.
  b Explain what job each part does.
5 What are ligaments? What do they do?
6 Some cartilage is smooth and slippery. Some is gristly. Say where you would find each kind.

2.5 Synovial joints

Most of your joints are freely moveable or **synovial joints**. They allow different kinds of movement, depending on the shape of the bones at the joint, and the ligaments that hold them together. These drawings show just the bones.

The ball-and-socket joint

This is the most moveable joint in the body. One bone has a bulge like a ball at the end. This fits into a socket in the other bone. It can turn in many directions.

Examples
- the hip joint
- the shoulder joint

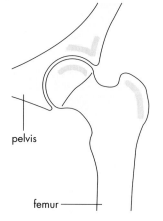

Hip joint

The hinge joint

This works like a hinge on a door. The bone can swing back and forward. The end of one bone is shaped like a spool of thread. It fits into a hollow in the other. The joint will open until it's straight, but no further.

Examples
- the elbow joint (between the humerus and ulna)
- the knee joint (between the tibia and femur)

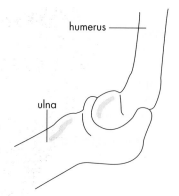

Elbow joint

The pivot joint

One bone has a bit that juts out, like a peg or a ridge. This fits into a ring or notch on the other bone. The joint allows only rotation.

Examples
- the joint between the atlas and axis (the top two vertebrae)
- the joint between the radius and ulna, below the elbow

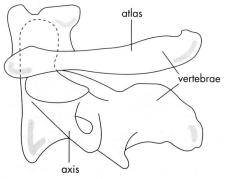

Joint in neck

The saddle joint

Here the ends of the bones are shaped like saddles and fit snugly together.

The joint allows movement back and forward and from side to side.

Example
- the joint at the base of the thumb between the metacarpal and a carpal. (It's the only saddle joint in your body.)

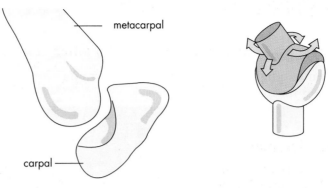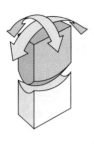

Joint at base of thumb

The condyloid joint

A rounded bump on one bone sits in a hollow formed by another bone or bones. The joint allows movement back and forward and from side to side. Ligaments prevent the bones from rotating.

Examples
- the joint at the wrist between the radius and carpals
- the joint between the base of the skull and the top vertebra (atlas)

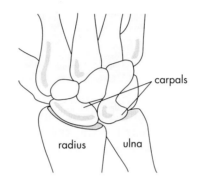

Joint at wrist

The gliding joint

Here the ends of the bones are flat enough to glide over each other. There is a little movement in all directions. Of all the synovial joints, this one gives least movement.

Examples
- the joints between carpals (in the hand)
- the joints between tarsals (in the foot)

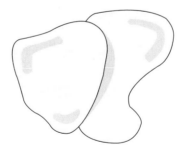

Joint between two carpals

Questions

1 The ball-and-socket joint is the most moveable.
  a Why do you think this is?
  b Where would you find one in your body?
  c Explain how it helps a tennis player.

2 Find the phalanges on your forefinger. How many hinge joints are there between them?

3 One joint allows you to turn your head.
  a Where is it?   b What kind of joint is it?

4 What's special about the joint at the base of your thumb?

5 One joint allows you to nod and tilt your head.
  a Where is it?   b What type of joint is it?

2.6 Some different movements

Flexion and extension

Extension means straightening a part of the body to its normal position. **Flexion** means bending it.

When you stand straight like this, your arms, legs, head, hands and feet are **extended** to their normal position.

Here the right arm is bent or **flexed** at the elbow joint. The left leg is flexed at the knee joint. Is the left ankle flexed?

When you run you repeatedly flex and extend your hip, knee, ankle, elbow and shoulder joints.

Some more examples of flexion:

 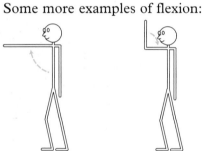  

arm at shoulder joint

arm at elbow and shoulder joint

leg at hip and knee joint

back at hip joints

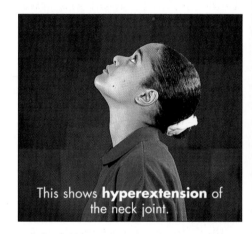

This shows **hyperextension** of the neck joint.

Abduction and adduction

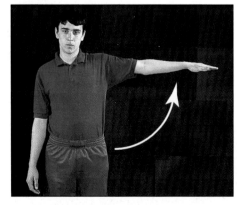

Imagine a line drawn down the centre of your body. **Abduction** is a sideways movement of a limb, out from the centre line.

Adduction is a sideways movement, like this, towards and even across the centre line. (**Ad**duction is towards the **midd**le!)

This karate kick is an example of abduction. Can you think of another example from tennis? Or from gymnastics?

Rotation and circumduction

These are circular movements.

Rotation is a turning movement around an imaginary line, like a wheel turning on its axis. Turning your head is an example.

This somersault is another example. The girl's body is rotating like a wheel on an imaginary axis.

In **circumduction**, the end of a bone moves in a circle. Swinging your arm in a circle is an example. Bowlers do it!

Joints and movement: a summary

In the last Unit you saw that different joints allow different kinds of movement. This is a summary of the kinds of movement they allow.

Type of joint	Movement allowed
ball-and-socket	flexion and extension abduction and adduction rotation and circumduction
hinge	flexion and extension
pivot	only rotation
saddle	flexion and extension abduction and adduction
condyloid	flexion and extension abduction and adduction
gliding	a little gliding in all directions (no bending or circular movements)

Questions

1 Sit straight in your chair, elbows by your sides, hands flat on your knees, feet flat on the floor.
   a Which joints are flexed?
   b Name two joints that are extended.
2 Stand up and show an example of:
   a adduction   b abduction
3 Stretch your arm out straight and show:
   a rotation at the shoulder joint   b circumduction
4 Rest your elbow on your desk and rotate your lower arm. Which joint allows this movement?
5 For the photo above: a name each numbered joint
   b name the movement at it.

Questions on Chapter 2

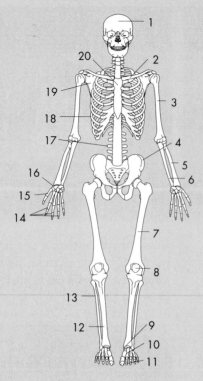

4 This shows the vertebral column with labels A to G.

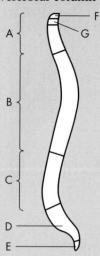

1 a Write the numbers 1 to 20 in a list, to match the numbers on the skeleton above.
   b Beside each number write the correct scientific name for the bone.

2 Copy this table. Then complete it by filling in the everyday names of the bones.

Bone	Everyday name
cranium	skull
scapula	
sternum	
clavicle	
femur	
phalanges (foot)	
metatarsals	
tarsals	
tibia	
patella	
phalanges (hand)	
metacarpals	
carpals	
coccyx	

3 Bones are long, short, irregular or flat. To which group do these bones belong?
   a the patella   **b** the carpals of the hand
   c the humerus   **d** the bones of the cranium
   e the metatarsals   **f** the vertebrae

a Copy this table.

	Name	Number of vertebrae	Description
A			
B			
C			
D			
E			
F			
G			

b In the second column, fill in the correct name for the labelled part. Choose from this list:
   lumbar vertebrae   axis   cervical vertebrae
   thoracic vertebrae   coccyx   atlas   sacrum

c In the third column, write the number of vertebrae in that part. Choose from this list:
   1   1   4   5   5   7   12

d In the fourth column, write the correct description. Choose from this list:
   allows the head to turn from side to side
   each vertebra connects with a pair of ribs
   forms a large triangular bone
   the largest and strongest vertebra
   the remnants of a tail
   vertebrae of the neck region
   allows the head to nod

5 Which *two* of these statements are correct?
The vertebral column is protected against damage by jarring because:
   A its shape makes it act like a spring
   B no movement between the vertebrae is allowed
   C the discs of cartilage act as shock absorbers
   D ligaments hold the vertebrae firmly in position

6 This drawing shows one vertebra:

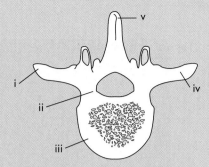

Which is correct?
The powerful muscles of the back are attached to parts:
A i and ii
B ii and iii
C iii and v
D iv and i

7 This question is about the vertebra shown above.
   a Which part of the vertebra supports the weight of the vertebrae above it?
   b Which part encloses the spinal cord?
   c What is this shape of bone called?

8 **a** Draw and label an adult long bone.
   b Now write down what job each part of the bone does.

9 Which is true of spongy bone?
   A The spaces are filled with marrow.
   B It is soft and spongy.
   C The spaces are filled with air.
   D The spaces are filled with air and marrow.

10 Explain how bones grow in length. Make drawings to help you.

11 As young bones grow, bone replaces cartilage.
   What is this process called?
   A ossification
   B osteoarthritis
   C osteopathy
   D osteoporosis

12 Answer these questions about bones.
   a Name a substance that is needed to form strong and healthy bones.
   b Give two examples of foods which will provide this substance.
   c What job does the cartilage on the ends of bones do?
   d Bones have spongy parts. How does this help you in playing sports?
   e In which part of the bone are red cells made?
   f Are red cells made in *all* bones?
   g Around what age does the skeleton stop growing?
   h How many vertebrae are in your back bone?

13 Which is correct?
   Most of the ligaments in the body attach:
   A bones to other bones
   B cartilage to cartilage
   C bones to muscles
   D tendons to bones

14 This shows a synovial joint, with parts numbered 1 to 4.

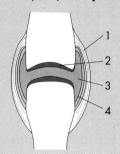

   a Copy this table:

Number	Name	Its function
1		
2		
3		
4		

   b Now complete the second and third columns of the table for each part of the joint.

15 The drawing below shows joints of the body.

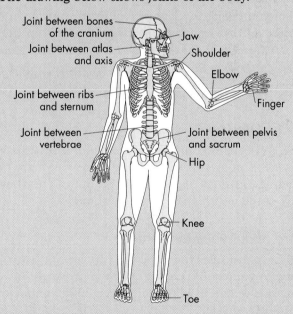

   a Make a table with five columns. Write these five headings on the columns:
   Fixed   Slightly moveable   Ball-and-socket   Hinge   Pivot
   b Now write each joint from the drawing in the correct column in the table.

27

3.1 Different kinds of muscle

You could not live without muscles. You couldn't breathe or digest food or even blink. They are involved in every movement of your body, inside and out.

All muscles work by shortening or **contracting**. When muscles between your mouth and jaw bones contract, you smile!

There are three different kinds of muscle in your body.

Voluntary muscle

This is attached to bones. It works when you want it to. *Voluntary* means *by your own free will*.

Suppose you decide to run or throw a ball. A signal races from your brain, along your nervous system, to the voluntary muscles needed for this job. The muscles contract, pulling on bones. This gives movement.

Voluntary muscle is also called:

- **skeletal muscle** because it is attached to bones
- **striped muscle** because when you look at it under a miscroscope you can see stripes across it.

Involuntary muscle

This is found in the walls of your internal organs: stomach, gut, bladder and blood vessels. It is called *involuntary* because it works on its own. You don't need to think about it.

When you digest food, the involuntary muscle in the walls of your gut contracts in waves, pushing the food along. In the same way, contractions in the walls of blood vessels help to keep blood flowing.

Involuntary muscle is also called **smooth muscle** because it looks smooth under a microscope, with no stripes.

Cardiac muscle

This is special involuntary muscle that forms the walls of your heart. It works non-stop without tiring. Like voluntary muscle, it is striped. When it contracts, it pumps blood out of your heart and round your body. Each contraction is a **heartbeat**.

More about voluntary muscle

Voluntary muscles form the red meat round your bones. They give shape to your body. Over 40% of your weight is voluntary muscle. So if you weigh 50 kilograms, over 20 kilograms of that is due to voluntary muscle.

The next page shows the main voluntary muscles in your body. Look at them and try to guess what they do when they contract. Then check in the list. For some actions, several muscles work together. For example when you swing your arm in a circle.

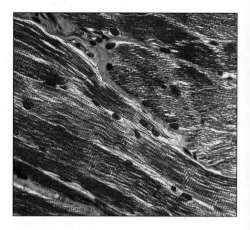

Voluntary muscle fibres, stained with dye to show up the stripes and magnified by 200.

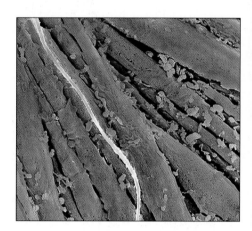

Smooth muscle fibres, magnified by 900. The pale wavy line is a nerve.

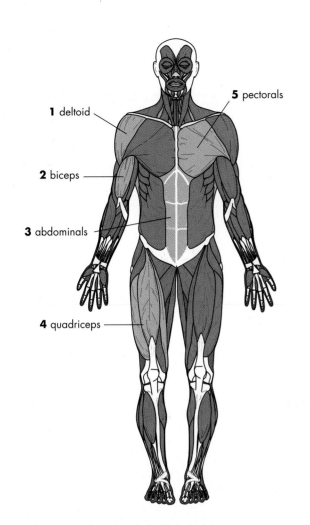

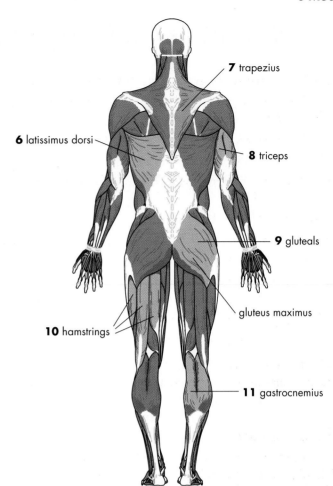

Muscle	Main action(s)
1 deltoid	Raises your arm sideways at the shoulder.
2 biceps	Bends your arm at the elbow.
3 abdominals (4 muscles)	Pull in your abdomen. Flex your trunk so you can bend forward.
4 quadriceps (4 muscles)	Straighten your leg at the knee and keep it straight when you stand.
5 pectorals	Raises your arm at the shoulder. Draws it across your chest.
6 latissimus dorsi	Pulls your arm down at the shoulder. Draws it behind your back.
7 trapezius	Holds and rotates your shoulders. Moves your head back and sideways.
8 triceps	Straightens your arm at the elbow joint.
9 gluteals (3 muscles)	Pull your leg back at the hip. Raise it sideways at the hip. Gluteus maximus is the biggest of these muscles.
10 hamstrings (3 muscles)	Bend your leg at the knee.
11 gastrocnemius	Straightens the ankle joint so you can stand on your tiptoes.

Questions

1 **a** Name the three kinds of muscle at work in your body as you answer this question.
   b Give examples of each of them.
2 What are the other names for voluntary muscle?

3 Where are these muscles and what job do they do?
   a pectorals   **b** biceps   **c** triceps
   d deltoids   **e** hamstrings   **f** quadriceps
4 Which muscle contracts when you look upwards?

29

3.2 Muscles and movement

How muscles work

A voluntary muscle usually works across a joint. It is attached to both the bones by strong cords called **tendons**.

When the muscle contracts, usually just one bone moves.

For example when the biceps in the arm contracts, the radius moves but the scapula does not.

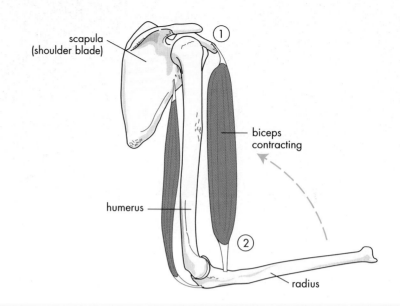

Origin and insertion

When a muscle contracts, usually just one bone moves. The other is stationary. The **origin** is where the muscle joins the stationary bone (1 in the diagram above). The **insertion** is where it joins the moving bone (2). When a muscle contracts, **the insertion moves towards the origin**.

Muscles working in pairs

Muscles usually work in pairs or groups. For example the biceps flexes the elbow. The triceps extends it.

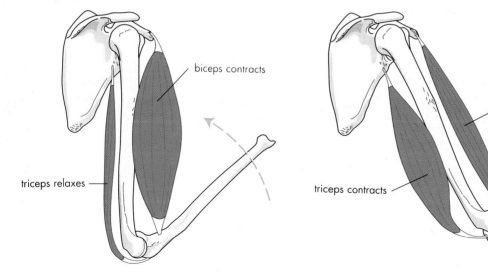

To flex the elbow the biceps **contracts** (shortens) and the triceps **relaxes** (lengthens).

To extend the elbow, the biceps relaxes and the triceps contracts.

This is called **antagonistic muscle action**. The working muscle is called the **prime mover** or **agonist**. (It's in agony!) The relaxing muscle is the **antagonist**.

Goal! To straighten the knee in the last stage of the kick, the quadriceps acted as agonist and the hamstrings as antagonist.

A network of muscles act as synergists to help hold her in position for this move.

The prime mover is helped by other muscles called **synergists**. These contract at the same time as the prime mover. They hold the body in position so that the prime mover can work smoothly.

Tendons

Tendons are the cords and straps that connect muscles to bones. They are white, flexible and very strong.

At the bone, the fibres of the tendon are embedded in the periosteum of the bone. This anchors the tendon strongly and spreads the force of the contraction. So the tendon won't tear away easily.

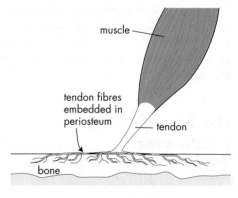

Muscle shape and size

Muscles come in many different shapes and sizes, depending on the job they have to do. Here are some examples.

Note the different shapes of tendons that go with them.

Note that the third one has two origins.

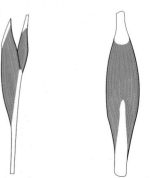

Questions

1 a Draw a diagram to show how the biceps works.
   b Why doesn't the humerus move?
2 a On which bone is the origin of the biceps?
   b On which bone is the insertion?
3 Where's the insertion of: **a** the triceps? **b** the deltoid?
4 Explain how this is helpful.
   a When a muscle contracts across a joint, usually just one bone moves.
   b Tendons are embedded in the periosteum.
5 'A muscle can have only one origin.' True or false?

3.3 Levers in your body

Making a lever

For thousands of years, men have used levers to help them move loads. Make one for yourself and try it.

You will need a pencil, a ruler, a rubber and a piece of thread about 15 cm long. Tie the thread around one end of the ruler, about 3 cm from the end. Now set up the lever as shown here.

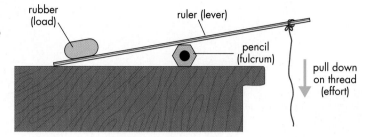

rubber (load)

ruler (lever)

pencil (fulcrum)

pull down on thread (effort)

What happens when you pull on the thread?

The ruler is the **lever**. The pencil is the pivot or **fulcrum**. The rubber is the **load**. You supply **effort** when you pull the end of the lever down.

There are three different types of lever, depending on the position of the fulcrum, load and effort. This one is called a **first-class** lever. Your body has examples of all three.

Levers in the body

In your body, muscles, joints and bones act together as lever systems:

- the lever is a bone. But it is not straight like your ruler!
- the fulcrum is usually a joint.
- the load is the weight of the body part being moved, plus any weight it is carrying (for example your arm plus tennis racket).
- effort is supplied by muscles contracting. The muscle tendons act like the thread in your lever.

First-class levers

Here the fulcrum is between the effort and the load.

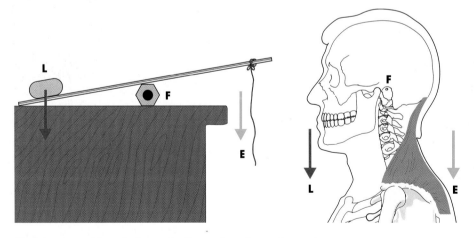

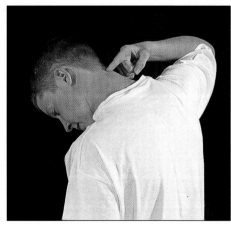

Put your finger on your neck like this and nod your head. You can feel the trapezius working.

Raising your head shows a first-class lever in action:

- the skull acts as the lever.
- the fulcrum is the joint between your skull and atlas.
- the load is the weight of the head. It pulls the head forward.
- the effort is supplied by the trapezius muscle. When it contracts it pulls the head back.

Second-class levers

This time the load is between the fulcrum and the effort.

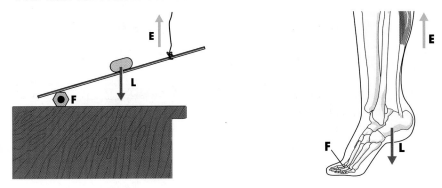

Standing on your toes shows a second-class lever in action:

- your heel bone acts as the lever.
- the fulcrum is the point of contact between the toes and ground.
- the load is the weight of your body.
- the effort is supplied by the gastrocnemius muscle that pulls on your heel bone. It is attached to it by the **Achilles tendon**.

Third-class levers

This time the effort is between the load and the fulcrum.

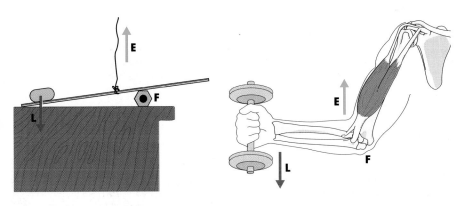

Lifting a weight shows a third-class lever in action.

- the radius and ulna act as the lever.
- the fulcrum is the elbow joint.
- the load is the weight of the lower arm, plus the weight being lifted.
- the effort is supplied by the biceps contracting.

With a third-class lever, the muscle is attached very close to the joint. So a small contraction produces a big movement. This makes these levers very useful. They are the most common type in your body.

Let your arm hang straight, then bend it like this. A contraction of just a few centimetres in your biceps raises your fist by about 60 centimetres. Third-class levers are very effective!

Questions

1 What does a lever do?
2 What does the fulcrum do?
3 Draw simple diagrams of these lever systems:
   a first-class b second-class c third-class

4 Beside each of your diagrams write down an example from your body.
5 Which is the most common type of lever in your body? Why is it so useful?

3.4 Muscle speed and tone

Muscle fibres

Muscles are made up of cells called **muscle fibres**. Muscles contract (shorten) because the fibres do.

But the fibres don't all contract together. The number contracting at any one time depends on how much force is needed.

For example more fibres in your biceps contract when you lift this book than when you lift a pencil.

There are two different kinds of muscle fibres, **slow twitch** and **fast twitch**.

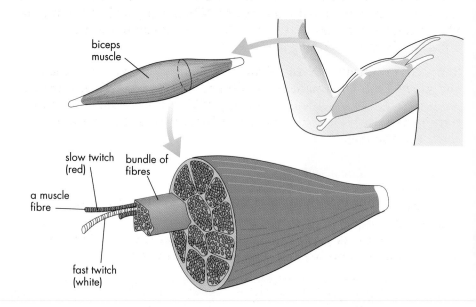

biceps muscle

slow twitch (red) bundle of fibres

a muscle fibre

fast twitch (white)

Fast and slow twitch fibres

Which sports are you best at? It partly depends on the mixture of slow and fast twitch fibres in your muscles.

Slow twitch fibres contract slowly, and without much force. But they do not tire easily. So they are suited to activities that need endurance. For example jogging, long-distance running, and standing for long periods.

Fast twitch fibres contract much faster than slow twitch fibres, and with much more force. But they tire quickly. So they are suited to activities that need bursts of strength and power. For example sprinting and weightlifting.

Every muscle contains a mixture of these fibres. But:

The mixture is different in different muscles. For example your gastrocnemius contains a lot of fast twitch fibre. Standing on your toes gets tiring!

The mixture is different for different people. Some distance runners have 80% slow twitch fibres while some weight lifters have 80% fast twitch.

Why the difference? It's all your parents' fault! You inherited the mixture from them and it's too late to change it now...

How muscle speed affects performance

The more fast twitch fibres you have, the more suited you are to sports that need bursts of strength and power. When you play just for fun, the fibre mix does not matter. But at higher levels it can make the difference between winning and losing.

Suppose two sprinters X and Y are competing. They are the same age and weight and at the same level of fitness. But X has 75% fast twitch fibre in her leg muscles and Y has only 55%. So X should be able to start faster, accelerate faster and sprint faster than Y. She has a better chance of winning.

Muscle tone

Even when a muscle is relaxed, a small number of its fibres are contracted - enough to keep the muscle taut but not enough to cause movement. This state of partial contraction is called **muscle tone**. Without muscle tone you could not stand up straight!

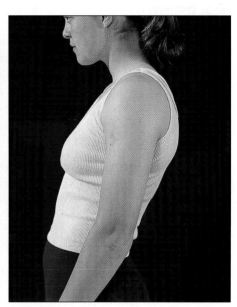

Gravity tries to pull your head forward, as shown here. But partial contraction or muscle tone in the trapezius will keep it upright.

Muscle tone in the quadriceps balances the muscle tone in the hamstrings to keep your legs straight at the knee.

If the muscle tone in your abdominals is poor, your spine curves in too much.
The result is poor posture.

To maintain muscle tone without getting tired, groups of muscle fibres take it in turn to contract. They work in relays.

Poor muscle tone leads to poor posture. But exercise improves muscle tone. It makes the muscle fibres thicker so they contract more strongly.

Questions

1 a What's another name for a muscle cell?
  b There are two different kinds. What are they?
2 Why is fast twitch fibre suited to weight lifting?
3 Why is slow twitch fibre suited to jogging?

4 Which type of fibre is suited to cross-country skiing?
5 What is *muscle tone*?
6 Without muscle tone you would collapse in a heap. Explain why.

3.5 Posture

The importance of good posture

Good posture means your body is in the position that puts **least strain** on your muscles, tendons, ligaments and bones.

The benefits of good posture

- It helps to make you and your clothes look good.
- It helps your heart, breathing and digestive system work properly.
- It helps prevent strain and injury in sport and other activities.
- It makes you less tired because you use less energy.

The penalties of poor posture

- You don't look as good as you could, no matter how great your clothes and hair are.
- Your muscles have to work harder so you get tired sooner.
- The strain on bones, tendons and ligaments can lead to injury. For example back strain and fallen arches.
- There's less space for your heart and lungs, which can interfere with their action. Round shoulders make it harder to breathe deeply.
- It can affect your digestion. Who wants that?
- Problems caused by poor posture can take years to put right.

Damage to the spine

The curves in your spine make it strong. But when they are out of shape, it is easily damaged. For example if you bend over to lift a heavy box, or twist violently, or develop poor posture.

Pressure on vertebrae can squash the cartilage disk so much that it presses on the spinal cord. This is called a **slipped disk**. It is very painful.

Good posture means less strain on muscles, tendons, ligaments and bones.

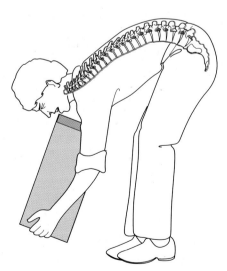

Lifting a heavy weight this way can damage your spine.

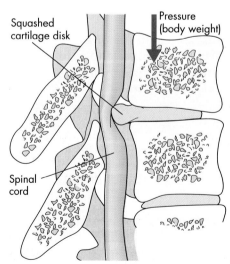

Squashed cartilage disk

Pressure (body weight)

Spinal cord

A section through two vertebrae showing a slipped disk.

High heels throw the body forward. Muscles work hard to straighten it again. That can be exhausting!

Practicing good posture

Whether you are sitting, standing, walking or lifting something, the main rule is:

Keep your spine as upright as possible, with its normal curves.

Good standing posture

- Head up, neck lengthened.
- Chin tucked in just a little.
- Spine stretched upwards.
- Chest high and open, so that you breathe freely.
- Arms loosely by your sides.
- Knees relaxed.
- Feet about 15 cm apart, with your weight evenly balanced between your heels and the balls of your feet.

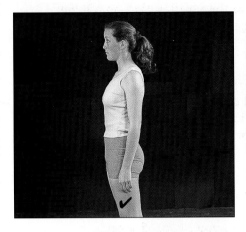 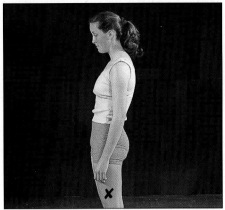

Good sitting posture

- Sit well back in your chair and let it support you.
- Spine and neck lengthened.
- Thighs straight in front of you.
- Feet flat on the floor in front of you (not under the chair).
- Arms relaxed.

When working at your desk:

- sit squarely in front of the desk
- bend forward from the hips instead of curving your spine.

Good lifting posture

- Stand directly in front of the object, close to it and with your feet apart.
- Bend your knees to reach it, keeping your spine straight.
- Use the full strength of your legs to help you lift it.

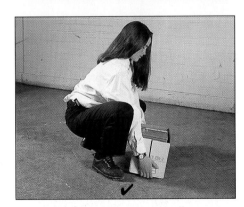 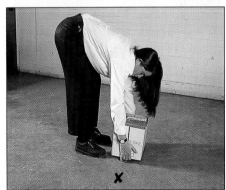

Questions

1. Give five reasons why poor posture is harmful.
2. Think of examples of sports where your spine is at most risk of injury.
3. What is the main rule of good posture?
4. Write posture instructions to tell someone:
   a how to lift a heavy suitcase
   b how to sit at the table to eat
   c how to walk upstairs

Questions on Chapter 3

1 Match the muscles in i - v below to A, B or C.
  A voluntary and striped
  B involuntary and striped
  C voluntary but not striped

  i cardiac muscle
  ii the muscle in your stomach walls
  iii the biceps
  iv the trapezius
  v the muscles in your artery walls

2 Match each statement i - vii below to A, B, C, D or E.
  A contraction
  B relaxation
  C muscles
  D muscle fibres
  E tendons

  i muscles try to return to their original length
  ii can be slow twitch or fast twitch
  iii are white, strong and flexible
  iv are usually joined to two bones across a joint
  v the muscle shortens
  vi more contract when you lift a heavy weight
  vii join muscles to bones

3 The drawings A to F below show different muscles.
  For each drawing:
  a Name the muscle.
  b Say where on your body:
    i the insertion is   ii the origin is.
    (You do not need to name the bones.)
  c Say what movement takes place when the muscle
    contracts. Use a word from this list:
      flexion extension adduction abduction rotation

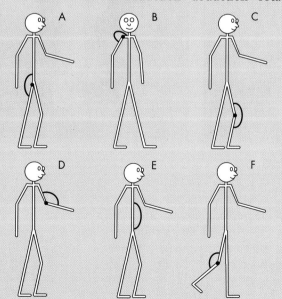

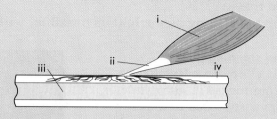

4 This shows where a muscle joins to a bone.
  a Name the numbered parts.
  b Part ii is embedded deeply in part iv.
    How does this help you?

5 Usually two muscles work together to move a bone.
  For example to flex your hip joint as in A below,
  one muscle contracts and another relaxes.

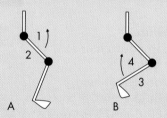

In drawing A:
  a Which muscle must contract to raise the thigh?
  b Which muscle must relax to allow this to happen?
  c Which is the agonist?
  d What other term is used for the agonist?
  e Which is the antagonist?
  f What is this kind of muscle action called?
  g What are the correct names for muscles 1 and 2?

In drawing B, the knee joint is being flexed.
  h Which muscle is the agonist this time?
  i Which is the antagonist?
  j Give the correct names for muscles 3 and 4.
  k Other muscles called synergists are also involved
    in these movements. What job do they do?

6 For actions a-d below, say which muscles you think are
  the agonists and which are the antagonists.
  (The drawings on page 30 will help you.)

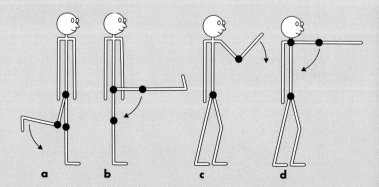

7

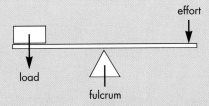

a A lever has only one purpose. What is it?
b A lever has a **load**, a **fulcrum** and an **effort**, as shown in the drawing above. Explain what these terms mean.

8 Copy these drawings of levers. Mark in the load (L) and effort (E). Then beside each drawing, write down an example from your body.

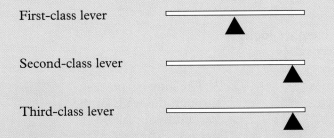

First-class lever

Second-class lever

Third-class lever

9 a Which kind of lever allows the biggest movement of the load for the smallest movement of the effort?
b Which kind of lever is the most common in your body? Why do you think this is?

10 Unless you are unconscious, your muscles are always partly contracted.
a What is this condition called?
b Explain how it helps you to hold your head up.
c Explain how it helps you to look better.
d Why do the muscles not get tired?

11 Each muscle in your body is a mixture of two types of muscle fibres, slow twitch and fast twitch.
a Which gives the strongest contractions?
b Which tires most easily?
c Which can keep going for longer?
d 'The more you exercise the more fast twitch fibre you have.' Is this statement true? Explain your answer.

12 Which type of muscle fibre do you depend on for:
a jogging?
b doing a back somersault?
c lifting a really heavy weight?
d carrying your books home from school?
e shot putting?
f working behind the counter in a shop?
g a 100 m swimming race?
h playing golf?
i pulling in a tug-of-war?
j playing a tennis match?

14 Name one muscle being exercised in each activity.

4.1 Energy for exercise

Movement is caused by muscles contracting. This needs **energy**.
Your muscles obtain energy from **food**. Food is a mixture of
carbohydrates, fats, proteins, vitamins, minerals and fibre. When you
eat, this is what happens:

- the food is broken down to a liquid in your gut. This is called
  digestion.
- the liquid food passes through the gut wall into your blood.
- the blood carries it to all your cells, including muscle fibres.
  The cells use it for energy, growth and repair.

How carbohydrates are digested

Your muscles use both carbohydrates and fats for energy. Here we look
just at carbohydrates. They are first broken down into **glucose**.

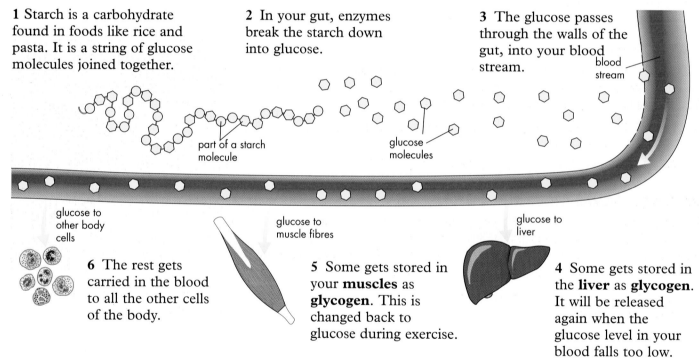

1 Starch is a carbohydrate
found in foods like rice and
pasta. It is a string of glucose
molecules joined together.

2 In your gut, enzymes
break the starch down
into glucose.

3 The glucose passes
through the walls of the
gut, into your blood
stream.

blood
stream

part of a starch
molecule

glucose
molecules

glucose to
other body
cells

glucose to
muscle fibres

glucose to
liver

6 The rest gets
carried in the blood
to all the other cells
of the body.

5 Some gets stored in
your **muscles** as
glycogen. This is
changed back to
glucose during exercise.

4 Some gets stored in
the **liver** as **glycogen**.
It will be released
again when the
glucose level in your
blood falls too low.

Cell respiration

Cells get energy from glucose in a process called **cell respiration**.
Two kinds of cell respiration go on in your muscle fibres.

Aerobic respiration. This uses oxygen to produce energy:

glucose + oxygen → energy + carbon dioxide + water

- Some of the energy is used by the muscles for movement.
- Most is produced as heat. That's why exercise warms you!
- Blood carries the carbon dioxide, water and heat away from the
  muscles. The carbon dioxide is **excreted** through your lungs.

Anaerobic respiration. This does not use oxygen:

glucose → ⟨energy⟩ + lactic acid

- This gives far less energy than aerobic respiration.
- When enough lactic acid builds up in your muscles, it acts like a mild poison. It causes pain and fatigue. Your muscles stop working.

Cell respiration during exercise

Your muscles usually get their energy from aerobic respiration - for example when you walk, jog, dance, swim or cycle.

But sometimes muscles need a lot of energy very fast - for example when you sprint. You can't provide enough by aerobic respiration because oxygen can't reach your muscles fast enough. So anaerobic respiration takes over.

But after less than a minute, the lactic acid stops your muscles working. If you try to keep on sprinting you will collapse.

For everyday activities like cycling to school, your muscles use oxygen to get energy.

Lactic acid and the oxygen debt

After strenuous exercise like sprinting, your muscles need extra oxygen to get rid of lactic acid. This extra oxygen is called the **oxygen debt**. You pay it off by gulping air into your lungs.

- Most of the lactic acid gets turned into carbon dioxide and water. This gives out a lot of energy.
- Some is changed back into glucose and glycogen.

Replacing glycogen

During hard exercise, muscle glycogen and some liver glycogen gets used up. These stores must be replaced. So athletes snack on bananas and other starchy foods as soon as exercise is over. It can take marathon runners several days to rebuild their glycogen stores.

You can find out more about replacing glycogen, and recovery from exercise, on page 95.

Gasping for air after a hard race, to repay the oxygen debt.

Questions

1 When carbohydrates are digested what substance is formed?
2 How does this substance reach your muscles?
3 What happens it there?
4 **a** What is *cell respiration*?
  b Name the two kinds that go on in muscle fibres.
  c Write a word equation for each type.

5 In a game of tennis you might use both types of cell respiration. Explain.
6 Write down *two* advantages of aerobic respiration, compared to anaerobic respiration.
7 **a** What is the *oxygen debt*?
  b How does it occur?
  c How do you repay it?

4.2 The respiratory system

The respiratory system

Your cells obtain energy by aerobic respiration. That needs oxygen. Your body takes it from the air via the **respiratory system**.

Air is drawn in through the nose, where it is filtered by tiny hairs and warmed and moistened by **mucus**.

The voice box or **larynx**, which makes sounds for speaking.

The windpipe or **trachea**. This is a flexible tube held open by rings of cartilage.

In the lungs, the trachea branches into two **bronchi**. Each is a **bronchus**.

The bronchi branch into smaller tubes called **bronchioles**.

The bronchioles end in bunches of tiny air sacs called **alveoli**. Their walls are so thin that gases can pass through them.

A small flap of cartilage stops food going into the windpipe instead of the gullet. It is called the **epiglottis**.

The lungs are soft and spongy.

The lungs are in a space called the **thoracic cavity**.

The **pleural membrane** is a slippery skin lining the cavity. It protects the lungs as they rub against the ribs.

The **ribs** protect the lungs.

The **intercostal muscles** between the ribs help you breathe in and out.

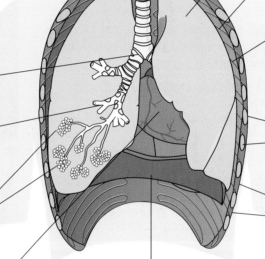

heart

The **diaphragm** is a sheet of muscle below the lungs. It helps you breathe in and out.

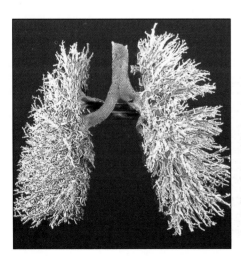

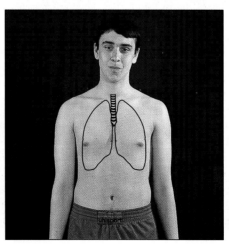

A resin cast of the lungs, and an outline of their position in the body. The green tubes in the resin cast are the ones that carry the blood supply.

The alveoli

Your lungs take in oxygen and give out carbon dioxide.
This **gas exchange** takes place in the alveoli of the lungs.

These are the alveoli at the end of a bronchiole. Each is smaller than a grain of salt.

The walls of the alveoli are thin and moist, which helps gases pass through.

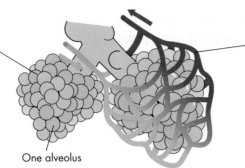

One alveolus

The alveoli are covered with tiny blood vessels called **capilliaries**. Gases can pass through the capillary walls.

Gas exchange in the alveoli

This shows what happens in the alveoli.

1 Blood carries waste carbon dioxide from the body cells to the alveoli.

2 The carbon dioxide passes through the capillary walls and into the alveoli.

3 From here it travels out of the lungs and up the windpipe. You breathe it out.

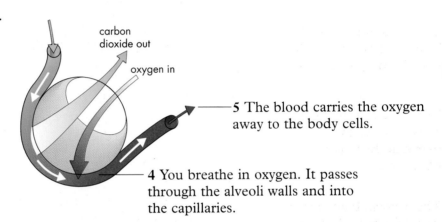

carbon dioxide out

oxygen in

5 The blood carries the oxygen away to the body cells.

4 You breathe in oxygen. It passes through the alveoli walls and into the capillaries.

How air changes in your lungs

In the lungs, oxygen is taken from air and carbon dioxide added to it.
So the air you breathe out is different from the air you breathe in.
This table shows the changes.

Gas	Amount in inhaled air (the air you breathe in)	Amount in exhaled air (the air you breathe out)
oxygen	21 %	17%
carbon dioxide	a tiny amount	3%
nitrogen	79%	79%
water vapour	a little	a lot

Look at nitrogen. The amount does not change. Can you explain why?

Questions

1 What job does the hair in your nose do?
2 What's another name for your windpipe?
3 What stops food going into your windpipe?
4 What job does the pleural membrane do?
5 Which two gases are exchanged in the lungs?

6 Where in the lungs does gas exchange take place?
7 The alveoli have very thin walls. Why is this useful?
8 Do you use all the oxygen you breathe in?
9 You breathe out the same amount of nitrogen as you breathe in. Why is this?

4.3 Breathing and exercise

Breathing is also called **external respiration** or just **respiration**. Don't confuse it with cell respiration! Breathing in is **inspiration**. Breathing out is **expiration**.

When you breathe in

Several changes take place.

1 The intercostal muscles contract. This pulls the rib cage upwards. So the chest expands.

2 The diaphragm contracts. This pulls it down and flattens it, making the chest even larger.

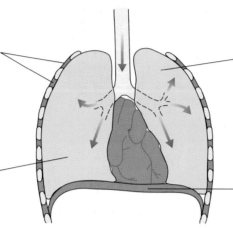

3 When the chest expands, the lungs expand too, because their moist surface clings to the chest lining.

4 When the lungs expand the pressure inside them falls. So more air is sucked down the windpipe and into the lungs.

When you breathe out

The opposite changes take place.

1 The intercostal muscles relax. This lowers the rib cage and makes the chest smaller.

2 The diaphragm relaxes so it bulges upwards again. This makes the chest even smaller.

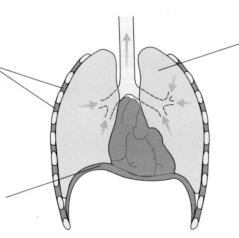

3 When the chest gets smaller, the lungs are compressed. So air is pushed out of the lungs and up the windpipe.

How much air do you breathe?

- The **tidal volume** is the amount of air you breathe in or out with each breath. When you breathe deeply it increases.
- The **respiratory rate** is how many breaths you take per minute.
- The **minute volume** is the amount of air you breathe in per minute.
  Minute volume = tidal volume × respiratory rate
  The larger it is, the more oxygen gets to your cells.
- The **vital capacity** is the maximum amount of air you can breathe out, after breathing in as deeply as you can. It is usually around 4.5 or 5 litres.
- The **residual volume** is the amount of air left in your lungs after you breathe out as hard as you can. It is usually around 1.5 litres. You can never empty your lungs completely.

Calculating your minute volume

Example

Tidal volume: 0.6 litres
Respiratory rate: 14 breaths a minute

So minute volume

= 14 × 0.6 litres a minute
= 8.4 litres a minute

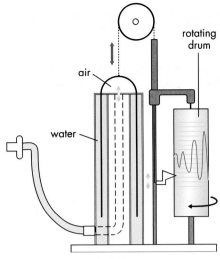
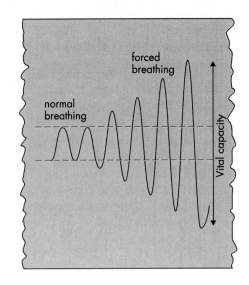

The volume of air you breathe in and out can be measured using a spirometer. When you breathe into the mouthpiece, the dome rises so the pen falls, marking a trace on the paper.

Your lungs and exercise

Your lungs and heart work as a team to get oxygen round the body and clear carbon dioxide away. When you exercise, your heart and lungs have to work harder. This is what happens:

1 During exercise, cell respiration in your muscles increases. So the level of carbon dioxide in your blood rises.

2 Your brain detects this. It sends a signal to your lungs to breathe faster and deeper.

3 So gas exchange in your lungs speeds up. More carbon dioxide passes out of the blood and more oxygen passes into it.

4 The brain also sends a signal to your heart to beat faster. So:

- more blood gets pumped to the lungs for gas exchange

- more blood gets pumped to the muscles, carrying oxygen and removing carbon dioxide.

Look how breathing changes during exercise:

For an 18-year-old ...	at rest	during exercise
tidal volume	0.5 litres	2.5 litres
respiratory rate	12 breaths a minute	30 breaths a minute
minute volume	6 litres a minute	75 litres a minute

Questions

1 What is: **a** inspiration? **b** expiration?
2 When you breathe in your chest expands.
   a Explain how this happens.
   b Explain why your lungs expand too.
3 Why does air leave the lungs when you breathe out?
4 What is: **a** tidal volume? **b** respiratory rate?
5 In the table above, how did exercise change:
   a the tidal volume? **b** the respiratory rate?
   c the minute volume?
6 Explain how these changes helped the person.

Questions on Chapter 4

1 Like other substances in food, carbohydrates are broken down during digestion. The substance that is produced can be used by your muscles for energy.
  a Name this substance.
  b Name the process by which energy is obtained from it.
  c Some of the substance is stored in your muscles. In what form is it stored?
  d Why is it stored in the muscles?
  e What happens to this store during exercise?
  f The substance is also stored in your liver. After a marathon run, your liver store of it will be low. Why do you think this is?

2 Copy and complete the paragraph below using words from this list. You can use a word more than once, or not at all.

  glycogen   pain   lactic acid   oxygen
  anaerobic   aerobic   respiration   carbon dioxide

  When muscles use _____ to obtain energy, the process is called _____ _____. When they don't use oxygen it is called _____ _____. But then it can continue for only a short time because _____ _____ is produced. This causes _____ and fatigue. The muscles stop working.

3 a Write down a word equation for aerobic respiration in your muscles using glucose.
  b Explain what happens to each substance that is produced.

4 a Write down a word equation for anaerobic respiration in your muscles using glucose.
  b Explain what happens to each substance produced.

5 Match each statement **i - ix** below to A, B, C or D. Choose the best match each time.
  A external respiration
  B cell respiration
  C inspiration
  D expiration

  i This process produces energy from glucose.
  ii The air moved in this process contains less oxygen than normal air.
  iii Oxygen is normally used for this process.
  iv This is another word for breathing.
  v During this you get rid of carbon dioxide.
  vi The air moved during this is called inhaled air.
  vii The air moved during this is called exhaled air.
  viii During this you take in oxygen.
  ix This can also take place without oxygen.

6 This diagram of the respiratory system has numbers but no labels.

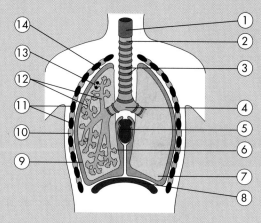

  a Write down the numbers 1 to 14 in a list.
  b Beside each number, write the correct label.
  c What is the purpose of the respiratory system?

7 Copy and complete the paragraph below, using words from this list. You may use a word more than once, or not at all.

  ribs   diaphragm   volume   decrease   exhaled
  relax   intercostal   lungs   expiration   heart

  During inspiration the _____ muscles contract and pull the _____ upwards and outwards. At the same time the _____ contracts, changing from a dome to a flatter shape. These movements cause the _____ to increase in _____. During _____ all these muscles _____, causing air to be _____.

8 Look at this table:

	% oxygen	% carbon dioxide
Inhaled air	21	0.03
Exhaled air during quiet breathing	17	3
Exhaled air during exercise	15	6

  a Why is there *less* oxygen in exhaled air than in inhaled air?
  b Why is there *more* carbon dioxide in exhaled air than in inhaled air?
  c Explain why the percentage of oxygen in exhaled air falls during exercise.
  d Explain why the percentage of carbon dioxide in exhaled air rises during exercise.
  e Exhaled air contains at least 15% oxygen. Explain why this makes the 'kiss-of-life' possible.

9 This shows apparatus students used to measure their vital capacity and tidal volume. The plastic container has been marked in litres.

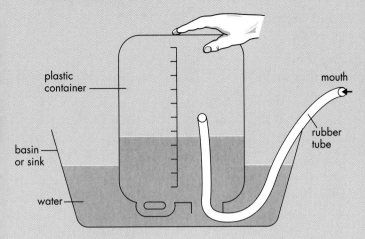

plastic container

mouth

rubber tube

basin or sink

water

a What is tidal volume?
b What is vital capacity?
c What will happen to the water level when you breathe in and out normally, through the rubber tube?
d Explain how you could use this to find your tidal volume.
e How would you use the apparatus to find your vital capacity?

10 A spirometer was used to record an athlete's breathing at rest and after exercise. Each wave (from one trough to the next) represents one breath. From the height of the wave you can tell the volume of air breathed in.

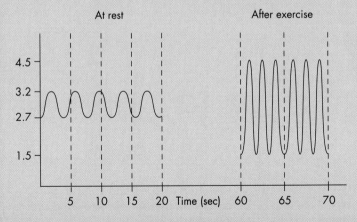

At rest   After exercise

a What was the athlete's tidal volume at rest?
b What was her tidal volume during exercise?
c How many breaths did she take per minute:
   i at rest? ii during exercise?
d What was her minute volume:
   i at rest? ii during exercise?
e Explain the difference between your answers for d.
f Inhaled air contains 21% oxygen. How much oxygen did the athlete breathe in per minute:
   i at rest? ii during exercise?
g Why was this change in oxygen needed?

Things to do

Here you will compare your tidal volumes (TV), respiratory rate (RR) and minute volumes (MV) during rest and exercise. You will need to work with a partner.

1 A table for your results

First, copy this table. You will use your copy to record your results.

During ...	TV (litres)	RR (breaths per minute)	MV (litres)
rest			
gentle exercise	1.5		
vigorous exercise	2		

2 Tidal volume

You can measure this using the method shown in question 9.
But do it only for your TV at rest.
(It is difficult to measure TV this way during exercise, so we have put two estimates in the table for you.)

a Set up the apparatus as shown in question 9.
b Breathe normally into the tube. The water level will rise and fall.
c Ask you partner to record the maximum and minimum water levels as accurately as possible.
d Then work out your TV. Record the result in your table.

3 Respiratory rate

This is the number of breaths you take per minute.
a Sit and relax for several minutes. Then, when your partner says 'Go', start counting your breaths. Your partner will tell you when one minute is up. Record the result in your table.
b Repeat the experiment, but this time count your breaths while jogging gently on the spot.
c Repeat the experiment, but this time jog hard on the spot, raising your knees high.

4 Minute volume

This is the volume of air you breathe in per minute.
Minute volume is given by this formula: $MV = TV \times RR$
Use the formula to complete the last column in your table.

5 Analysing the results

a How have your TV, RR and MV changed with exercise?
b Why are these changes needed?
c Compare your results with those of the rest of the class. Why do some people have higher minute volumes? Do you think it depends on build? Or on fitness?
d Through training, you can increase your minute volume. Why would this be useful?
e Which muscles in particular must grow in strength for this increase to occur?
f Suggest an exercise you could use for this purpose.

5.1 The circulatory system

Your blood works non-stop, 24 hours a day. It carries food and oxygen to your body cells. It carries carbon dioxide and other waste away.

Blood is pumped round the body by the **heart**. It flows along tubes called **blood vessels**. The blood, heart and blood vessels together make up your **circulatory system**.

A first look at the circulatory system

This is a simple plan of your circulatory system. It shows just the heart and four main blood vessels:

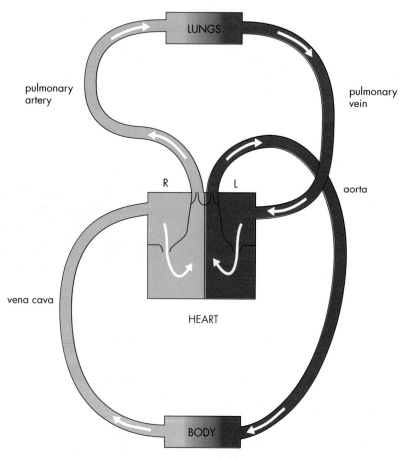

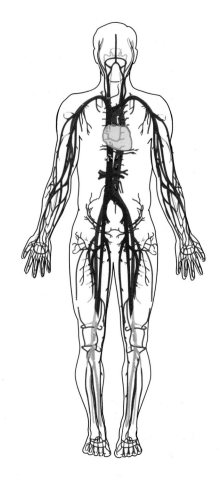

The main arteries and veins in the body. The arteries are shown in red, the veins in blue.

- Notice how the heart is divided into two parts. Each part is a pump, so the heart is a **double pump**.
- The right part pumps blood to the lungs to pick up oxygen.
- The left pumps this **oxygenated** blood around the rest of the body.
- The large tubes that carry blood *a*way from the heart are called **arteries**. The **aorta** is the largest artery.
- The large tubes that carry blood back to the heart are called **veins**. The **vena cava** is the largest vein.
- **Pulmonary** means *to do with the lungs*.
- The **pulmonary artery** carries blood from the heart to the lungs to pick up oxygen. It's the only artery carrying **deoxygenated** blood.
- Four valves control the blood flow through the heart. You will find out more about these in the next Unit.

Blood flow from the heart

R	→	lungs	→	L
L	→	body	→	R

Note that R is shown on the left since the diagram is facing you.

How the blood is carried round your body

Every time your heart beats it pumps blood at high pressure into the arteries.

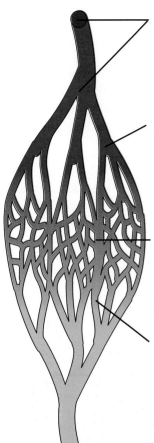

1 An **artery**. Its walls contain elastic tissue and muscle. The blood stretches the walls. Then the walls contract and force the blood along.

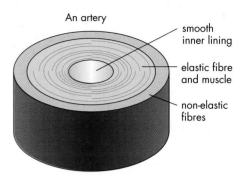

An artery

- smooth inner lining
- elastic fibre and muscle
- non-elastic fibres

2 The artery branches into smaller tubes called **arterioles** ...

3 ... which branch into very tiny tubes called **capillaries**. Their walls are so thin that food and oxygen can pass out to the body cells. Carbon dioxide and other waste can pass in.

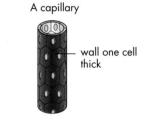

A capillary

- wall one cell thick

4 From the capillaries the blood flows into larger tubes called **venules**. It has given up its oxgen. It is **deoxygenated**.

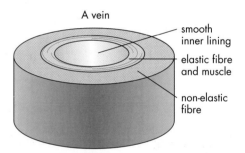

A vein

- smooth inner lining
- elastic fibre and muscle
- non-elastic fibre

5 From the venules it flows into a **vein**, which will carry it back to the heart.

The valves in veins

By the time blood reaches the veins it is flowing more slowly, at lower pressure. So veins have valves to make sure it can't flow backwards.

Many large veins are inside your leg and arm muscles. When the muscles contract, they squirt the blood towards your heart.

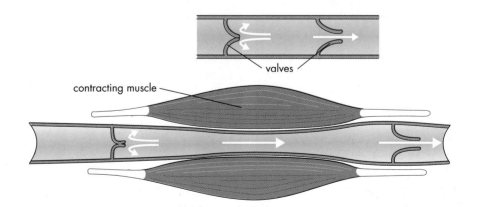

valves

contracting muscle

Questions

1 The heart is a double pump. Explain.
2 Which type of large blood vessel carries blood:
   a away from the heart? b to the heart?
3 All the arteries except one carry oxygenated blood. Which artery is the exception? What does it do?

4 Compare an artery, a vein and a capillary. Which:
   a is widest inside?
   b has a thick layer of muscle and elastic tissue?
   c has valves? Why does it need them?
   d has very thin walls? Why is this useful?

5.2 How the heart works

Inside the heart

This is a simple drawing of the inside of your heart.

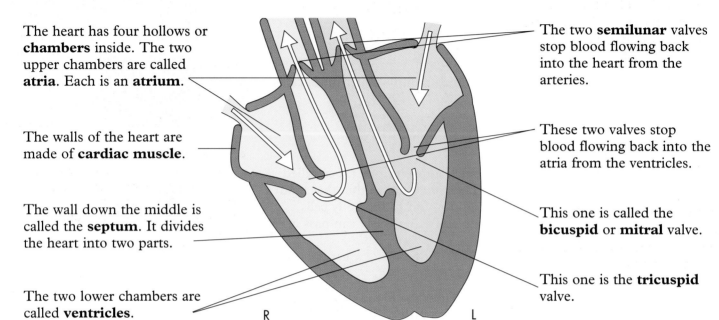

The heart has four hollows or **chambers** inside. The two upper chambers are called **atria**. Each is an **atrium**.

The walls of the heart are made of **cardiac muscle**.

The wall down the middle is called the **septum**. It divides the heart into two parts.

The two lower chambers are called **ventricles**.

The two **semilunar** valves stop blood flowing back into the heart from the arteries.

These two valves stop blood flowing back into the atria from the ventricles.

This one is called the **bicuspid** or **mitral** valve.

This one is the **tricuspid** valve.

R   L

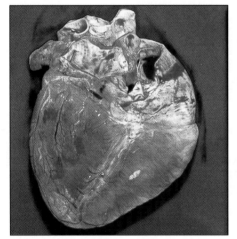

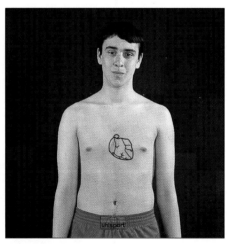

The heart: what it *really* looks like, and where to find it in the body. It nestles between your lungs, protected by the ribs.

The cardiac muscle

The walls of your heart are made of cardiac muscle. When this contracts the heart gets smaller so blood gets pumped out.

The right side pumps deoxygenated blood to the lungs, at low pressure. The left pumps oxygenated blood all round the body, at much higher pressure. This needs more force, so the left side has thicker walls.

Now look at the left ventricle. It has the thickest walls, because it works hardest of all. When it contracts, it pumps blood into the aorta and round the body.

How the heart pumps blood

The heart pumps blood by **contracting**. It does this in two stages.
First the atria contract. Then about a tenth of a second later the
ventricles contract. This shows what happens:

1 When the heart is relaxed, both
sides fill with blood from the veins.
(But no blood can flow in from the
arteries. Can you see why?)

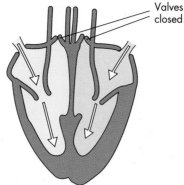

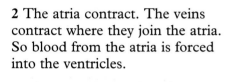

2 The atria contract. The veins
contract where they join the atria.
So blood from the atria is forced
into the ventricles.

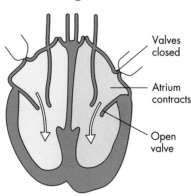

A closed semilunar valve. When the
ventricles contract in step 3 below, the
spurt of blood will force these three
flaps open. The blood will rush
through the valve (towards you) into
the artery.

3 Then the ventricles contract. The
valves between the ventricles and
atria close. So the blood is forced
out of the heart, into the arteries.

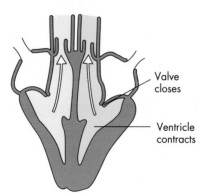

4 The heart muscle relaxes again
and steps 1 – 3 are repeated.

This cycle of events is called the **cardiac cycle**.
One complete contraction and relaxation is called a **heart beat**.
Your heart beats around 70 times a minute when you are resting.
This can rise to 200 beats a minute when you run very fast.
The number of beats per minute is called your **heart rate**.

Questions

1 What are the heart walls made of?
2 What are the two upper chambers called?
3 What are the two lower chambers called?
4 What is the inner wall called?
5 What do the valves do?

6 Where would you find: **a** the bicuspid valve?
   b the tricuspid valve? **c** a semilunar valve?
7 Where are the heart walls thickest? Why?
8 Where are they thinnest? Why?
9 What is: **a** the cardiac cycle? **b** a heartbeat?

5.3 What's in blood?

Blood is a liquid called plasma, with red cells, white cells and platelets floating in it. You have nearly 5 litres of it in your body – enough to fill 8 or 9 milk bottles!

Plasma

Plasma is a yellowish liquid. It is mostly water, with different things dissolved in it. The dissolved substances include:

- glucose and other nutrients from digested food
- hormones
- carbon dioxide and other waste from cells.

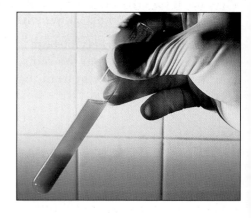

This blood sample has just been centrifuged. The yellow liquid is plasma. The red cells have collected at the bottom of the tube.

Red cells

Red cells are the body's oxygen carriers. They contain a red substance called **haemoglobin** which combines readily with oxygen. Haemoglobin gives the cells their red colour.

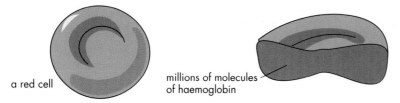

a red cell

millions of molecules of haemoglobin

The red cells are made in red marrow in some bones (mainly the ribs, vertebrae, humerus and femur). You have an enormous number of them: around 5 million *in each drop of blood*.

How red cells carry oxygen

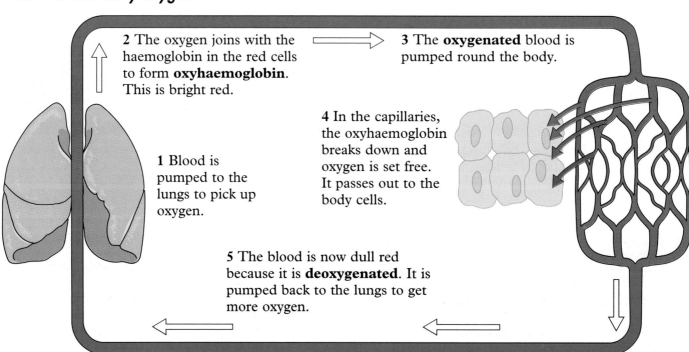

2 The oxygen joins with the haemoglobin in the red cells to form **oxyhaemoglobin**. This is bright red.

3 The **oxygenated** blood is pumped round the body.

4 In the capillaries, the oxyhaemoglobin breaks down and oxygen is set free. It passes out to the body cells.

1 Blood is pumped to the lungs to pick up oxygen.

5 The blood is now dull red because it is **deoxygenated**. It is pumped back to the lungs to get more oxygen.

White cells

White cells defend your body against disease.
They are larger than red cells, and have a nucleus.
There are several different kinds of white cell, all doing different jobs.
For example white cells called **phagocytes** eat up germs:

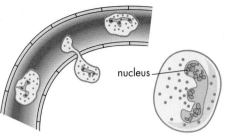

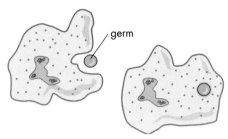

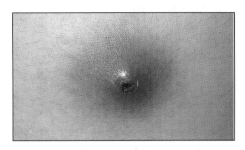

1 The phagocytes pass out through capillary walls and into the infected tissue.

2 They change shape to surround the germs. They produce enzymes to kill and digest them.

3 Phagocytes live for only a short time. Dead phagocytes, dead germs and liquid form **pus** in the infected area.

Other white cells make **antibodies**. These are chemicals that destroy germs. Different germs need different antibodies.

White cells are made in your red bone marrow, lymph nodes and spleen. Your blood has far fewer white cells than red ones. But when you are ill, more white cells are produced to help you fight infection.

Platelets

Platelets are fragments from special cells made in red bone marrow. They stick to each other easily. Their job is to stop your body losing blood. They do this making the blood **clot**. This is how they work:

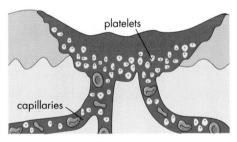

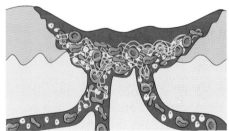

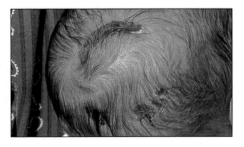

1 When you cut your hand, platelets stick to the surface of the wound and to each other.

2 They produce a substance that makes tiny fibres grow. Red cells get trapped in these. A clot forms.

3 The clot hardens to a scab, like on this head wound. It will drop off when new skin grows.

Questions

1 What is blood?
2 What is the main substance in plasma?
3 Name three other substances in plasma.
4 a What is the job of red cells?
  b What substance helps them do this job?
  c How does this substance work?

5 One kind of blood cell has a nucleus. Which one?
6 What is the job of white cells?
7 White cells called phagocytes eat up germs. Explain how they do this.
8 What are antibodies? What produces them?
9 Explain how platelets stop a cut bleeding.

5.4 What blood does

Your blood has two jobs: to carry things around the body and to protect you against infection.

What blood carries

Your blood is like a non-stop delivery service. It picks things up in one part of the body and carries them to another part.

Blood carries	How
1 oxygen from the lungs to all your body cells	in red cells
2 carbon dioxide from the cells to the lungs for excretion	mainly in plasma
3 other waste, and excess water, from cells to the kidneys for excretion	in plasma
4 glucose and other nutrients from the gut to the cells	in plasma
5 hormones from the hormone glands to the parts that use them	in plasma
6 white blood cells to infected places	floating in plasma
7 heat from warmer to cooler parts of the body and to the skin for removal	all parts of the blood

How blood protects you

Germs are **bacteria** and **viruses** that cause disease. They can enter your body through your lungs, through cuts, and in food and water. The platelets and white cells in blood protect you.

- Platelets cause blood to **clot**. This stops germs getting into cuts.
- If germs do get into your body, some white cells eat them up. Others make antibodies to destroy them.

If the germs are ones your white cells have not met before, it may take the white cells some time to make an antibody. But once they have done it, they can do it faster next time. If the germs return they are destroyed immediately. You become **immune** to the disease.

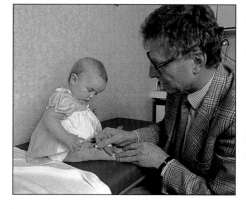

Immunization. The baby is being injected with a weak form of the bacteria that cause meningitis. Her white cells will develop antibodies, making her immune to the disease.

Questions

1 Blood does two jobs. What are they?
2 Name two things carried in blood:
   a which are gases. How does the blood carry them?
   b which the body will get rid of (excrete).
3 What are germs?
4 Name two things in blood that protect you.
5 If you catch measles once, you won't catch it again. Explain why.

5.5 Blood pressure

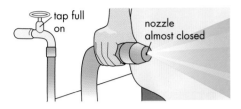 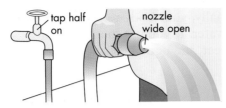 

When the tap is full on, and the nozzle nearly closed, the water pressure in a hose is very high. High enough to damage plants.

Now it is much lower. The pressure depends on how much water flows into the hose and how easily it can flow out.

Blood pressure is the same. It depends on how much blood flows into a blood vessel and how easily it can flow out.

That's why blood pressure is different in different blood vessels.

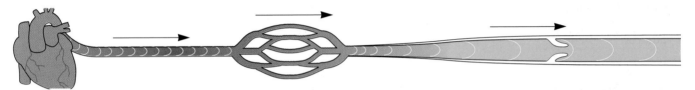

It is highest in the arteries. The blood pumps in fast, but it can't flow out through arterioles easily because they are so narrow.

It is lower in the capillaries, because the blood flows into them more slowly and then flows out to wider tubes.

It is lowest in the veins because the blood drains into them quite slowly and they are the widest blood vessels.

Measuring blood pressure

Blood pressure is always measured at an artery in your arm. It is measured using a rubber cuff attached to a thin tube of mercury.

The blood pressure in the artery rises when your heart contracts and falls when it relaxes. Both values are measured. Normal blood pressure is around 120/80. You say this as **120 over 80**. It means that the pressure is 120 mm when the heart contracts and 80 mm when it relaxes. (120 mm and 80 mm are the height of the mercury in the tube.)

Blood pressure and exercise

When you exercise, your heart beats faster and pumps out more blood. So your blood pressure rises. If it rises too much it is dangerous. Your body takes action to prevent this.

For example the brain sends a message to the arterioles to open wider. This reduces blood pressure. But it also helps you in another way. Now more blood gets to your muscles faster, carrying oxygen for respiration.

Measuring blood pressure. The doctor pumps up the cuff until the pressure inside it just equals the pressure in the artery. He can tell by listening through the stethoscope. As the cuff is pumped up, the mercury rises in the tube.

Questions

1 Why is blood pressure highest in arteries?
2 Explain why blood pressure is lowest in veins.
3 Where in the body is blood pressure measured?

4 If you cut an artery the blood pumps out in spurts. If you cut a vein it seeps out steadily. Try to explain this difference.

5.6 Blood, heat and water

Your body does not like change. Normally, your body temperature is 37 °C and your blood is about 50 % water. If you get too hot during exercise, or lose too much water in sweat, the body takes action to get back to normal.

If you get too hot

Exercise makes you warm. This is because cell respiration in the muscles increases, giving out heat. Blood carrries the heat around your body. But when your temperature starts to rise, this is what happens:

1 Blood vessels under the skin expand. This is called **vasodilation**. Now more blood flows near the surface. It loses heat by **radiation**. Just like a radiator!

2 The sweat glands make more sweat. This is mainly **water**. Heat from your body makes it **evaporate**, which helps to cool you.

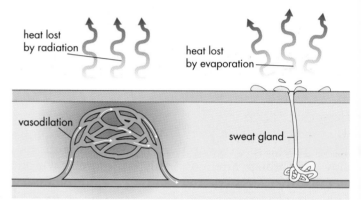

When you exercise on a hot dry day you can lose a lot of water as sweat. If the air is hot and *humid*, sweat will not evaporate. Your temperature may rise out of control. This is called **heat stroke** and it can kill you.

If you get too cool

If your body temperature drops below 37 °C, your body tries to stop it getting colder:

1 You stop sweating.

2 The blood vessels under the skin contract. This is called **vasoconstriction**. Now less blood flows near the surface so less heat is lost.

3 Your muscles may start to **shiver**. This produces heat.

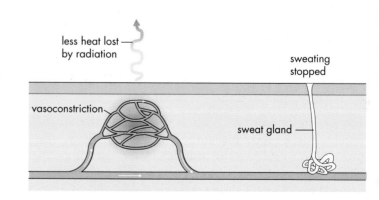

But if you get cold enough, your reactions slow down. You lose control of your hands and you can't walk properly. You can't think straight. You are suffering from **hypothermia**. It can kill you.

Water in the body

- Your body **takes in** water in food and drink.
- It **produces** water during cell respiration.
- It **loses** water in urine, sweat, your breath and faeces.

Kidneys and water control

The kidneys are your body's main water control centre.

The kidneys filter all your blood about 300 times a day.
They excrete waste substances and water as **urine**.

If you take in more water than you need, the kidneys make more urine.

The less water you take in, the less urine they make.

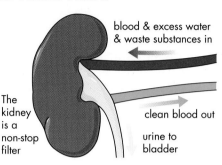

blood & excess water
& waste substances in

The kidney is a non-stop filter

clean blood out

urine to bladder

If you stop taking in water, the kidneys will soon stop making urine. But then the waste substances will build up in your blood and poison you.

How thirst helps

When you lose a lot of water, your brain reminds you to drink by making you feel thirsty.

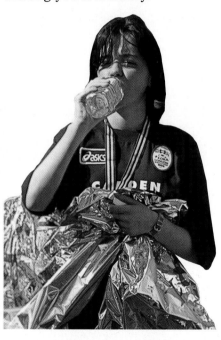

1 When you exercise hard, you sweat a lot to cool down. So your body loses water.

2 Because your body has less water, less saliva forms in your mouth. Your mouth gets dry.

3 Your brain detects this and makes you feel thirsty. So you drink. The amount of water in your body rises again.

You can lose up to 3 litres of sweat an hour. So make sure you drink plenty of water during and after exercise. If you don't you may suffer from **dehydration** which makes you weak and dizzy.

Questions

1 Why does exercise warm you up?
2 What is normal body temperature?
3 What is *vasodilation*? Explain how it helps to cool you down.
4 Skin reddens during exercise. Think of a reason.
5 How does shivering help you?

6 What is:
  a heat stroke?
  b hypothermia?
7 List the four ways your body loses water.
8 Explain how your kidneys help to regulate body water.
9 Why should you drink water during and after exercise?

5.7 The circulation and exercise

How well does your heart pump?

- **Heart rate** is the number of times the heart beats a minute.
- The **stroke volume** is the amount of blood that leaves a ventricle each time the heart beats. (The amount is the same for each ventricle.)
- The **cardiac output** is the amount of blood that leaves the left ventricle in one minute, to be pumped round the body.
- So **cardiac output = stroke volume × heart rate**

Calculating your cardiac output

Example

Heart rate: 68 beats a minute

Stroke volume: 75 ml per beat

So cardiac output
= 75 × 68 ml a minute
= 5100 ml a minute
= 5.1 litres a minute

How to measure your heart rate

At each heart beat, blood is pumped into your arteries. It makes the artery walls expand. Then they contract. One expansion and contraction is called a **pulse**.

You can feel pulses at several points in your body. By counting the pulses you can tell your heart rate.

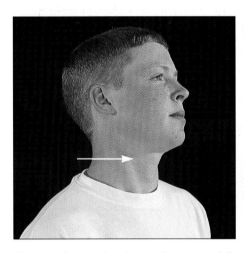

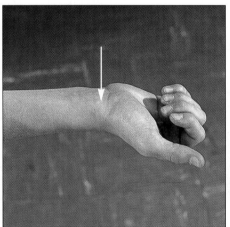

One **pulse point** is on the **carotid** artery in your neck, in the groove beside your windpipe. Either side will do! See if you can find it.

Another is on the **radial** artery at your wrist, below the thumb. To take your pulse, you need a watch with a seconds hand.

Press lightly on the pulse point with your first two fingers. Note the time. Start counting. Stop when a minute is up.

The number of pulses in one minute equals your heart rate – around 70 when you are resting. Now run on the spot for a minute and take your pulse again. What is it this time? What does that tell you?

Stroke volume

Stroke volume also increases during exercise. This is why.

- Contracting muscles squeeze on your veins, which causes more blood to squirt back to the heart.
- So the heart gets fuller. That makes its fibres stretch more.
- Because its fibres are more stretched, the heart contracts more strongly - just like when you stretch an elastic band. A stronger contraction pumps out more blood.

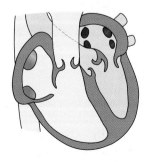

The fuller the heart gets, the more its fibres stretch.

How the body changes during exercise

You saw on page 45 how your lungs and heart work harder during exercise. Here we look again at those changes and add some more.

1 During exercise, cell respiration in your muscles increases. So the level of carbon dioxide in your blood rises.

2 Your brain detects this. It sends a signal to your lungs to breathe faster and deeper.

3 So gas exchange in your lungs speeds up. More carbon dioxide passes out of the blood and more oxygen passes into it.

4 The brain also sends a signal to your heart to beat faster. Your **heart rate** goes up.

5 Your muscles squeeze on veins, sending more blood back to the heart. This makes **stroke volume** rise.

6 So **cardiac output** rises too. More blood gets pumped to the muscles each minute.

7 This means more oxygen reaches the muscles each minute and more carbon dioxide is carried away.

Note these changes too:

8 Arterioles widen so that your blood pressure won't get too high.

9 Blood gets shunted from where it is less needed to where the action is. For example from your gut to your legs.

To make this happen, blood vessels widen and constrict at different points (vasodilation and vasoconstriction).

10 The exercise generates heat. So your blood gets hotter. More blood is shunted close to the skin to cool down. This makes your skin redden.

11 You sweat, which cools you by evaporation.

This table shows how the heart works harder during exercise:

For an 18-year-old ...	resting	during hard exercise
heart rate (HR)	70 beats a minute	200 beats a minute
stroke volume (SV)	70 ml per beat	150 ml per beat
cardiac output (CO)	4.9 litres a minute	30 litres a minute

Changing ml to litres

1000 ml = 1 litre

so just divide the number of ml by 1000 to change to litres:
4900 ml = 4.9 litres

Questions

1. What is: **a** heart rate? **b** stroke volume?
2. What is a *pulse*?
3. Give two example of pulse points in the body.
4. What is your heart rate if your pulse count is:
   a 100 for 60 seconds? **b** 70 for 30 seconds?
   c 12 for 10 seconds?

5. Why does stroke volume increase during exercise?
6. When you exercise, some blood is shunted to where it is needed more. Give an example.
7. Calculate the cardiac output when:
   a HR is 70 beats a minute, SV is 110 ml per beat
   b HR is 150 beats a minute, SV is 150 ml per beat

Questions on Chapter 5

Question hints: the heart and circulation

To answer questions about the heart and circulation, start by scribbling a diagram like this.

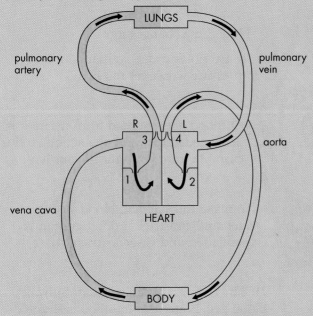

1 First draw a square box for the heart. Now draw a line down the middle to represent the septum. Mark the two halves R and L for *right* and *left*. (You are facing the drawing so R is on your left!)

2 Draw two more boxes, for the body and lungs.

3 Draw in the blood vessels and direction of blood flow. Remember, it flows *out* beside the septum.

R → lungs → L (**R**on loves **L**ondon)
L → body → R (**L**essons **b**ore **R**on)

4 Label the blood vessels. Remember:
- **arteries** carry blood *a*way from the heart.
- **veins** carry blood to it.
- the main artery from the heart is the **aorta**.
- the main vein to it is the **vena cava**.
- **pulmonary** means to do with the lungs.

5 Now draw in the four valves in the heart.
- 1 and 2 separate the upper and lower chambers of the heart. They are the **cuspid** valves.
  - 1 is called the **tricuspid** valve.
  - 2 is called the **bicuspid** or **mitral** valve.
- 3 and 4 lead *out* of the heart.
  - They are the **semilunar** valves.

6 The upper chambers of the heart are the **atria**. The lower chambers are the **ventricles**. Write these labels on.

---

1 Scribble a simple diagram of the heart and circulation by following the instructions on the left. Practice until you can do it in less than **2** minutes.

2 a What is *oxygenated* blood?
  b Name a blood vessel where you would find it.
  c What is *deoxygenated* blood?
  d Name a blood vessel where you would find it.
  e Only one artery carries deoxygenated blood. Which one?
  f Where does blood get oxygen?
  g Only one vein carries oxygenated blood. Which one?
  h A red substance in blood picks up the oxygen. What is the name of this substance?

3 On a scribble diagram from 1:
  a shade the oxygenated blood red
  b shade the deoxygenated blood blue.

4 Look at the drawing of the heart below. It has numbers 1 to 11, but no labels.

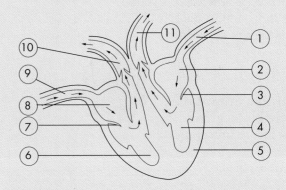

  a Write the numbers 1 to 11 as a list.
  b Beside each number write the correct label.

5 When blood leaves the heart and travels around the body it passes through these blood vessels:
  1 veins
  2 arteries
  3 capillaries
  4 arterioles
  5 venules

  In which order does it pass through them?

  A 1, 5, 3, 4, 2
  B 1, 2, 4, 3, 5
  C 2, 4, 3, 1, 5
  D 2, 4, 3, 5, 1

60

6

valve

This shows a valve in a vein. Which is its job?
A to close the vein after each heartbeat
B to keep the vein open at all times
C to stop blood flowing backwards
D to stop blood flowing too fast

7 This shows a vein and muscle in your leg.

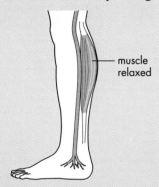

muscle relaxed

a How will the shape of the muscle change when it contracts to let you run forward?
b What effect will this have on the vein?
c What effect will it have on your heart?
d Arteries don't need this kind of help from muscles. Why not?
e Why do veins need this kind of help?
f If you sit still for a long time, your legs will feel heavy and swollen. Why is this?
g How would you cure the problem?

8

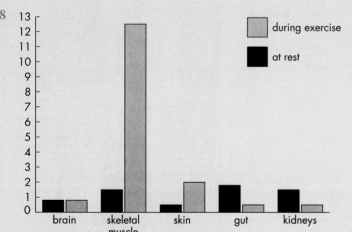

during exercise

at rest

This shows how the blood flow to different parts of your body changes during exercise.

a Explain how and why exercise affects blood flow to:
  i your skin   ii your muscles
  iii your gut   iv your kidneys
b Blood flow to your brain is undisturbed by exercise. Why is this important?

9 Match each statement i - viii below to A, B, C or D. Choose more than one letter if you need to.
A platelets
B red blood cells
C white blood cells
D plasma

i fight germs
ii have a nucleus
iii mainly water
iv stick together easily
v can pass through capillary walls
vi are the biggest blood cells
vii make blood clot
viii carries glucose and hormones

10 Explain how each of these helps you.
a You sweat a lot during exercise on a hot day.
b Blood vessels under the skin dilate during exercise.
c Blood may get shunted from your gut to your legs during exercise.
d You shiver when it gets cold.
e You feel thirsty after exercise.

11

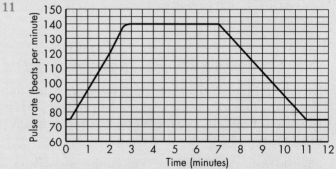

This graph shows how a teenager's pulse rate changed during an 8-minute run.
a What was his resting pulse rate?
b How long did it take his pulse to reach its maximum value?
c Why did his pulse speed up?
d Did he run at a steady speed, or did he vary it? Explain why you think so.
e After the run was over, how long did it take for his pulse to return to normal?

12 a What is: i stroke volume? ii cardiac output?
b How would you expect these to change during the run in question 11? Explain why.
c Copy and complete this table for the boy:

	Resting	Maximum value during exercise
Heart rate		
Stroke volume	70 ml	150 ml
Cardiac output		

61

6.1 What is fitness?

Fitness is the ability to meet the demands of the environment. If you are fit, you can cope with all your tasks and activities without getting too tired, and still have energy left for emergencies.

Fitness is divided into two areas, **general** and **specific**.

General fitness

General fitness concerns the day-to-day working of your body. It has several aspects:

- **Stamina** or **endurance**. This is the body's ability to keep going for long periods without getting tired. It is made up of:

  1 cardiovascular endurance. This is the ability of your heart to deliver oxygen to your muscles over long periods of exercise. Since the lungs are also involved it is sometimes called **cardiorespiratory endurance**.

  2 muscular endurance. This is the ability of your muscles to maintain and repeat contractions without getting tired.

  The two are related, because your muscles will tire easily if they do not get enough oxygen.

  Many activities need both kinds of endurance. For example stacking shelves all day long in a shop, swimming or jogging.

- **Strength**. This is the force muscles exert when they contract. You need strength to lift a suitcase or push in a rugby scrum. If you have too little strength you risk injury when you lift, pull or push things.

- **Flexibility** or **suppleness**. This is the range of movement at a joint. You need flexibility for tying your shoe laces, reaching up to a shelf, or playing sports. If you have poor flexibility you move stiffly, and are more likely to injure your tendons and ligaments in violent movements.

- **Speed**. This is the time taken to move the body or part of the body over a given distance. You need to move quickly to avoid traffic, catch buses and chase the ball in a football match.

General fitness and health

General fitness is sometimes called **health-related fitness** because it helps to keep you healthy. It helps to protect you against accidents, heart disease, stress, muscle injury and other health problems.

We all need a minimum level of general fitness, just to cope with everyday life. For sport, you need a higher level of fitness in at least some areas. For example a gymnast needs lots of strength. Does he or she also need speed? Or flexibility?

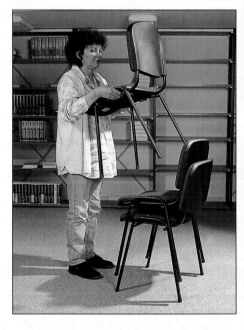

Fetching, carrying, stacking. All in a day's work for some people, and all demanding general fitness.

This needs an exceptionally good sense of balance...

... and this needs high explosive strength.

Specific fitness

General fitness will help you play a sport better. But to be really *good* at it you also need specific fitness in at least some of these areas.

- **Power** or **explosive strength**. This is a combination of strength and speed. You need power to hit the ball hard in tennis or throw the discus or do a karate chop.

- **Agility**. This is the ability to change the body's position and direction quickly. You need to be agile when playing squash, for example. It helps you avoid injury as well as hit the ball.

- **Balance**. This is the ability to hold a posture without wobbling or falling over, for example when you are standing on one leg. Gymnasts and ice skaters need a good sense of balance.

- **Co-ordination**. This is the ability to move your body parts smoothly and accurately in response to what your senses tell you. For example when you return a serve at tennis.

- **Speed of reaction**. This is the time it takes you to respond to a stimulus. For example how long it takes you to start running in response to the starting pistol. Fast reactions are a big advantage in most sports.

- **Timing**. This is the ability to act at the right moment. For example you need to judge the best time to tackle your opponent on the football field, or return a hard shot in tennis.

Specific fitness is also called **skills-related fitness**. Why?

Questions

1 Write down another word for *endurance*.
2 There are two different kinds of endurance.
   a What are they? **b** How they are related?
3 Who do you think needs greater flexibility?
   a a building worker **b** a gymnast **c** a hurdler
4 Who do you think needs greater strength?
   a a rugby player **b** a swimmer **c** a golfer

5 **a** leg power **b** balance **c** good co-ordination
   d fast reactions **e** good timing **f** agility
   Match each of these to a sport or sports where it is important. Choose from this list:
     sprinting   rugby   swimming   canoeing
     pole-vaulting   skiing   judo   golf
6 Why is specific fitness called *skills-related* fitness?

6.2 Factors affecting fitness

How fit are you right now? That depends on several factors.
Not all of them are under your control!

1 Age

You are usually at your fittest in your twenties. This graph shows fitness
in terms of oxygen used per kilogram of body weight. The more you
use, the fitter you are (page 68).

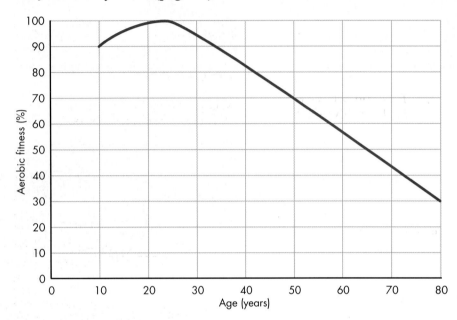

From your thirties onwards, fitness
falls because:

- muscles get weaker
- bones get lighter
- heart rate decreases
- joints get stiffer
- movements get slower
- body fat increases.

But exercise can slow these changes
down and even reverse them.

2 Sex

Up to about 11, males and females are equal in terms of general fitness.
But things change from then on ...

- **Strength**. Males grow about 50% stronger than females because they
  have more muscle. The male hormone **testosterone** promotes the
  growth of muscle and bone. It is released at puberty.

- **Cardiovascular endurance**. Males are better than females at
  transporting oxygen. They have larger hearts and lungs and more
  blood. Their red blood cells contain more haemoglobin, which is the
  oxygen carrier.

- **Bone structure**. Males are usually larger and heavier than females
  because they have bigger bones. They also have a narrower pelvis.
  This makes it easier to transmit power between the legs and trunk,
  which is an advantage in most sports.

- **Speed**. Because they have longer bones and bigger muscles, males
  can move faster. This means they also generate more power.

- **Flexibility**. Females score higher for flexibility. Females of all ages
  tend to be more flexible than males.

- **Body composition**. Females usually have more body fat than males.
  Fat acts as padding and keeps you warm, but it is extra weight to
  carry round. It puts extra strain on the heart, joints and muscles.

3 Physique

Your build and shape make you fitter for some sports than others.
A tall thin person is probably more suited to basketball than boxing.
Find out more about sport and build in the next Unit.

4 Diet

Your body needs certain substances for energy, growth and repair.
You get them from food. If you don't eat a healthy diet your body won't function properly.
You can find out about eating for fitness on pages 100-105.

5 Exercise

No matter how unfit you are, regular exercise will make you fitter.
Discover how training affects your body on pages 88 and 89.

6 Physical disability

A **disability** means part of your body does not function properly.
But exercise can keep the rest of the body very fit. Many disabled people are first-class athletes.

7 Illness and fatigue

When you are tired or ill you are less fit for any activity.

8 Drug-taking

Alcohol, cigarettes and many other substances lower your fitness.
See pages 106-109 for more about drugs.

9 Stress

Exams, quarrels, overwork, money problems - all these can lead to stress. Continual stress will affect your health, causing high blood pressure and heart disease. It is also linked to cancer.

Short term stress can affect your perfomance in sports events.
Your muscles are tense, you can't concentrate, you make mistakes.
One good way to deal with stress is to practice **relaxation**.

10 The environment

Fumes from traffic and factories, over long periods of time, will damage your lungs and make breathing difficult. This means your fitness suffers.

Your performance in a sports event is also affected by the environment.
For example on a hot, humid day you can overheat, which makes you weak and dizzy. And think what a windy day can do to a tennis match.

At high altitudes the air is 'thinner', so you must breathe harder to get enough oxygen. To perform well in sport at high altitudes you first need time to adapt.

Mustapha Badid of France, a world champion wheelchair athlete.

In windsurfing, wind speed has a dramatic effect on performance.

Questions

1 About what age are people usually at their fittest?
2 Explain how males and females differ in terms of:
   a strength b oxygen transport c body fat
3 How might stress affect your performance in sport?
4 Explain how pollution can affect fitness.
5 Could a person be fitter at 40 than at 20? Explain.

6.3 Somatotyping

Would you make a good gymnast? Or a good wrestler?
Success in a sport depends to a large extent on your build.

Somatotyping is a way to describe build. It looks at how fat, how
muscular and how linear you are, in that order. Each is measured on a
scale of 1 to 7. This shows the extreme examples:

Extreme **endomorph**	Extreme **mesomorph**	Extreme **ectomorph**
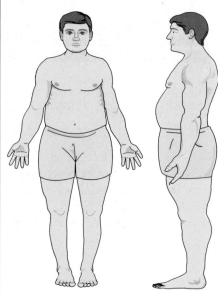	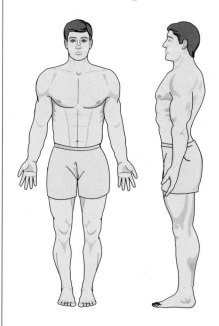	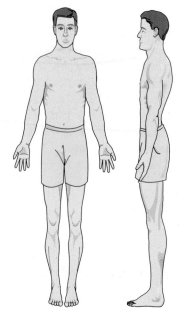
• wide hips and narrow shoulders (pear-shaped) • a lot of fat on the body • a lot of fat on the upper arms and thighs • quite slim wrists and ankles	• broad shoulders and narrow hips (wedge-shaped) • a large head • a muscular body • strong forearms and thighs • very little body fat	• narrow shoulders and hips • a thin face and high forehead • a thin narrow chest and abdomen • thin legs and arms • very little muscle or body fat
Somatotype rating: **7 1 1.**	Somatotype rating: **1 7 1.**	Somatotype rating: **1 1 7.**

Mesomorphs have **m**uscles. E**ct**omorphs are **t**hin and often **t**all.
Endomorphs stay pear-shaped even when they lose weight.

What's your rating?

Most people are between these extremes. Most have
a rating such as 3 4 4, or 3 5 2, or 4 3 3.

Finding your rating means taking some very complex
measurements. But you can at least have a guess.
What do you think yours is?

You inherit your basic build from your parents.
But you can change it to some extent through
exercise and diet.

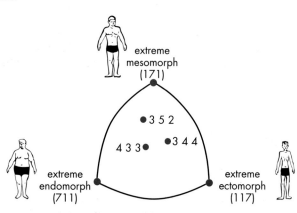

Somatotypes can be shown on
a somatochart like this one.

66

What's the ideal build for a sport?

For high jumpers, being tall and light is an advantage. But they also need strong muscles for power and lift. The ideal build: ectomorph with some mesomorph.

A sumo wrestler needs to be heavy so that he's hard to push or lift. He needs strength and power to move his opponent. Endomorph with some mesomorph is ideal.

Being light is an advantage for a gymnast. But she needs strong muscles to lift herself and hold a position. The ideal build: ectomorph with some mesomorph.

Somatotyping top athletes

This chart shows average ratings for top male athletes.

extreme
mesomorph
(171)

weight lifter
wrestlers
weight throwers
water polo players

gymnasts
rowers
sprinters
swimmers
distance runners
basketballers
race walkers

extreme
endomorph
(711)

extreme
ectomorph
(117)

They are all towards the mesomorph end. That proves the importance of muscle at this level! As you'd expect, weight lifters, wrestlers and weight throwers are more endomorphic than other athletes.

Questions

1 What is *somatotyping*?
2 Which body build has: **a** most muscle?
   b most fat? **c** least muscle and fat?
3 Can you change your build completely? Explain.

4 What do you think would be the ideal build for:
   a a hurdler? **b** a long jumper? **c** a jockey?
5 Top distance swimmers tend to have more body fat than top gymnasts do. How might this help them?

6.4 Testing aerobic fitness

The most important factor in fitness is the ability of your heart-lung team to deliver oxygen, and your muscles to use it. This is called **aerobic fitness**. Can you see why?

The higher your aerobic fitness:

- the lower your pulse rate, both during and after exercise
- the further and faster you can run without tiring.

A distance runner with high aerobic fitness may have a resting pulse rate as low as 40 bpm. To find out about *your* aerobic fitness, try one of these four tests!

The Harvard step test

Equipment
- a stepping bench or chair (around 50 cm high)
- a stop watch

Method
1 Step on the bench at a rate of 30 steps a minute for 5 minutes. If you can't keep up, stop after 20 seconds of slower steps.
2 Rest for 1 minute, then take your pulse for 15 seconds.
3 Your aerobic fitness is worked out using this formula:

$$\text{score} = \frac{\text{length of exercise in seconds} \times 100}{5.5 \times \text{pulse count}}$$

The *higher* it is, the fitter you are. Can you see why?

The Harvard step test.

The cycle ergonometer test

Equipment
- an exercise bike
- a stop watch

Method
1 Warm up on the bike for one minute, with no load on the pedal.
2 Now set the pedal speed to 60 revolutions per minute. Set the load to 150 watts if you are male, 100 watts if you are female.
3 Pedal for exactly 5 minutes.
4 20 seconds before the end, take your pulse for exactly 15 seconds. The lower it is, the fitter you are.

The Cooper test

Equipment
- a measured running track, in the gym or outside
- a stop watch and whistle

Method
1 Jog on the spot to warm up.
2 When the whistle goes, start running round the track as fast as you can. Your laps will be counted.
3 The whistle will go again when 12 minutes are up. Stop running. The further you ran in the time, the fitter you are.

The cycle ergonometer test.

68

The multistage fitness test

This measures your **maximal oxygen consumption** or **$\dot{V}O_2$max**. This is the maximum volume of oxygen you are able to use when exercising. The larger the value, the fitter you are.

A large person will generally use more oxygen than a small person, because he or she has larger muscles. To get around this, $\dot{V}O_2$max is usually expressed in *litres of oxygen per kilogram of body weight*.

To measure $\dot{V}O_2$max, you could go to a sports lab with special equipment. There you would exercise on a treadmill or exercise bike linked to a computer, with a tube to collect the air you breathe out. *Or* you could do the test below. It compares well with the lab test.

Equipment
- a distance of 20 metres marked out on the ground with sticky tape
- a tape recorder and a tape with bleeps recorded on it
  (The bleeps start slow but speed up each minute. The slowest are called level 1, the fastest are level 23.)

Method
1 Run 20-metre shuttles between the lines of sticky tape. Your foot should be on or across the sticky tape each time the bleep sounds.
2 When the bleep speeds up you must speed up too.
3 Stop when you can't keep up with the bleep. The level and the number of shuttles you did at that level are recorded.
4 Your teacher will then work out your $\dot{V}O_2$max from a table. The higher it is the fitter you are.

Using fitness tests

When you start on a fitness training programme, fitness tests are a useful way to check how your fitness is improving. Don't worry if you score less than your classmates. Your aim is to improve, and exercise is the key.

- Make a record sheet like this to write your scores in.
- Do the tests at regular intervals, for example every six weeks. Talk to your teacher about it.
- Make sure you do them correctly, and in exactly the same way each time. (Why?)
- Remember, if you are tired or ill your score will be affected.

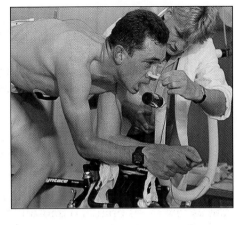

Sophisticated equipment is used to measure $\dot{V}O_2$max in the lab. At school you can use the multistage fitness test (below) which is much simpler.

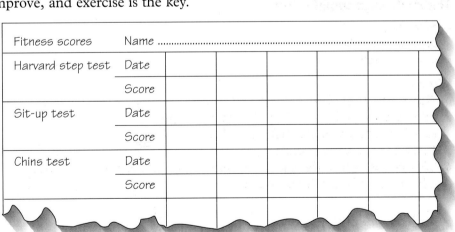

Fitness scores	Name					
Harvard step test	Date					
	Score					
Sit-up test	Date					
	Score					
Chins test	Date					
	Score					

Questions

1 What is *aerobic fitness*?
2 Pulse rate is a measure of aerobic fitness. Why?
3 What is $\dot{V}O_2$max? Which test is used to measure it?
4 In what units is $\dot{V}O_2$max usually given?

6.5 Other tests for general fitness

These tests will test other aspects of your general fitness. The higher the scores, the fitter you are. Repeat the tests at intervals. Record the scores in your record sheet and watch how they improve!

A test for grip strength

Equipment
- a hand-grip dynamometer

Method
1 Squeeze on the dynamometer as hard as you can with your preferred hand, for at least two seconds.
2 Do three times and record the highest reading of the three.

A test of your 30-metres sprint speed

Equipment
- a 30-metre distance marked out on a level non-slippery surface
- a stop watch

Method
1 Stand about 20 metres behind the start line.
2 At 'Go', sprint as fast as you can from there to the finish line.
3 Your partner will record your speed in seconds, from the moment you cross the start line.

The sit-up test

This tests the strength and endurance of the abdominal muscles.

Method
1 Lie on the floor with your hands touching your head above the ears, knees bent at 90°, and feet flat on the floor.
2 Get your partner to hold your feet down.
3 Raise your trunk until your elbows are past your knees. Then lower yourself to the floor again. This is one sit-up.
4 Do as many as you can in 30 seconds. Your partner keeps check of the time. Record your result.

Testing grip strength using a hand-grip dynanometer.

The sit-up test.

The chins test

This tests the strength and endurance of arm and shoulder muscles.

Equipment
● a chinning bar

Method
1 Hang from the bar with your palms facing inwards.
2 Raise yourself until your chin is level with the bar. Then lower yourself until your arms are straight again.
3 Repeat until you are too tired to do any more chins. Record how many you did.

The chins test.

The sit-and-reach test

This tests the flexibility of your hip joints.

Equipment
● a gymnastics bench
● a metre ruler
● sellotape

Method
1 Turn a bench on its side. Sellotape the ruler on top so that it extends 15 cm over the edge, with the zero nearest you.
2 Get a partner to hold the bench steady.
3 Sit with your feet flat against the bench, legs straight.
4 Slowly reach forward as far as you can and hold.
5 Your partner notes where your fingertips reach on the ruler.
6 Subtract 15 to find how far they have stretched beyond your heels. Record your result.

The sit-and-reach test.

Questions

1 Why start *behind* the line in the 30-m sprint?
2 What does this activity test?
  a sit-ups b chins c sit-and-reach
3 Describe in your own words a test for flexibility.

4 Make up a test to measure endurance for:
  a your biceps muscles
  b your gastrocnemius muscles
Check your tests with your teacher.

6.6 Some tests for specific fitness

The tests in this Unit are related to specific skills you need in sport.
A high score in a test will show your potential for some sports.
But to be *good* at a sport you also need lots of other things, including
motivation and plenty of practice!

The vertical jump test

This tests the power or explosive strength of your muscles.
You need good leg power for sports such as high jump, long jump,
basketball and netball.

Equipment
- a high wall
- talcum powder
- a vertical jump board if available

Method
1 Dip the palm of your preferred hand in talcum powder.
2 Stand sideways to the wall with your feet flat on the ground.
   Stretch your hand up as high as you can. Touch the wall or vertical
   board so that you leave a talc mark behind. (If using a board,
   arrange it so that you *just* touch the bottom of the scale.)
3 Dip your palm in talc again.
4 Now flex your knees and jump as high as you can, making a second
   mark as high up as possible.
5 Repeat three times. Work out how high you jumped each time.
   Record the best height of the three.

The vertical jump test.

The 5-metre shuttle

This tests your speed and agility. You need both of these for ball sports.

Equipment
- a running lane 5 metres long and 1.2 metres wide, marked out with
  sticky tape. It should be level and not slippery.
- a stop watch

Method
1 Warm up by jogging on the spot. Then get ready at the start line.
2 At 'Go', sprint as hard as you can to the end line and back. Both feet
   must cross both lines. This is one cycle.
3 Do five cycles altogether, turning as fast as you can each time.
4 Your total time is recorded in seconds.

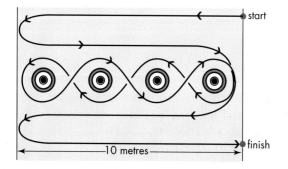

The 5-metre shuttle can be made more challenging with the help of
plastic cones. Arrange the cones like this and run the route as fast as
you can. A good test of agility!

The ruler drop test

This tests the speed of your reactions. Fast reactions are an advantage in most sports.

Equipment
- metre ruler

Method
1 Your partner holds the zero end of the ruler.
2 Place your hand close to the ruler, but not touching it, at the 50 cm mark as shown.
3 Your partner lets go without warning. You must catch the ruler between your thumb and first finger.
4 Record the reading on the ruler just above your first finger. Work out how far the ruler had dropped before you caught it.

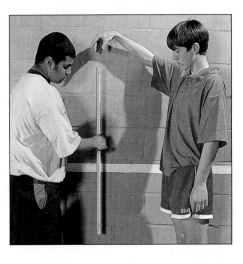

The ruler drop test.

A balance test

This is a test of your balance when standing on one leg.

Equipment
- a gymnastics bench
- a stop watch

Method
1 Stand on one foot on the bar - whichever foot you prefer.
2 Hold the other foot high behind your back, using the nearest hand.
3 Stand for as long as you can. The attempt ends when you touch the floor or let go the foot you are holding.
4 Keep trying until one minute is up. Record how many attempts you made.

A balance test.

A test of co-ordination

This tests your hand-eye co-ordination.

Equipment
- two tennis balls

Method
1 Hold a tennis ball in each hand. Start bouncing both balls at the same time.
2 Count how many times you can bounce both together without making a mistake.
3 Record the best score of two attempts.

Question

1 A high score in the vertical board test means you will be good at high jump. Is this true ? Explain.
2 a What is *agility*?
   b Explain why the 5-metre shuttle tests agility.
3 Name two sports that need good balance.
4 Name two sports that need good hand-eye co-ordination.
5 Make up a test to test your partner's speed of reaction, using only a tennis ball. Write instructions for the test. Then discuss it with your teacher.

Questions on Chapter 6

1 There are two kinds of fitness.
   a What are they called?
   b What is the difference between them?
   c Give two examples of each kind of fitness.

2 To be successful in sport you need both general and specific fitness. For example strength and agility are both important in rugby.

   Name one aspect of general fitness, and one of specific fitness, which is important in this sport:
   a cricket   b netball
   c judo   d golf
   e trampolining   f rock climbing
   g canoeing   h table tennis
   i throwing the discus   j football

3 Now name one aspect of general fitness and one aspect of specific fitness which is important for:
   a a circus clown
   b a juggler
   c a trapeze artist
   d a ballet dancer
   e a farm worker
   f a firefighter
   g a swimming pool attendant
   h a checkout operator in a supermarket

4 a What is *flexibility*?
   b Give three examples of the need for flexibility in your everyday life.
   c How would flexibility help:
      i   a sprinter?
      ii a high jumper?
      iii a weightlifter?
   d Do you think all sports people need flexibility? Explain.
   e Do you think sprinters need to be equally flexible in all their joints? Explain.

5 Cardiovascular fitness is one of the most important aspects of general fitness.
   a What is it?
   b What's another name for it?
   c Why is it so important?
   d If you were unfit in this way, what problems would it cause you in sport?

6 a Name three factors that affect your fitness which are not under your control.
   b Name three factors affecting fitness which are under your control.

7 Young boys and girls compete against each other in sport. But young adult males and females do not. Explain why.

8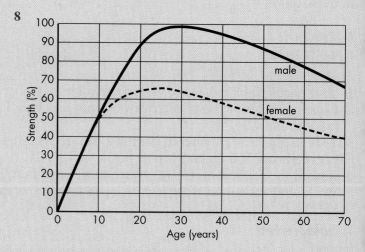

The graph above shows how strength changes with age for people who don't do much exercise.
   a From the age of 11 onwards, males become stronger than females. Why is this?
   b Around what age are both at their strongest?
   c Why do people lose strength as they get older?
   d By the age of seventy, people have lost a lot of strength. Give three examples of problems this might cause in everyday life.
   e What can you do to slow down strength loss as you get older?

9 On one graph, draw two curves to show how a person's fitness will change with age:
   a if the person is an inactive couch potato from the age of sixteen
   b if the person takes regular exercise through life.
   Your graph can be for either a male or a female.

10 a What is body composition?
   b How do males and females differ in terms of:
      i   body fat?
      ii   muscle?
      iii bone?
      iv   volume of blood?
      v   amount of haemoglobin?

11 A comparison of world records for male and female athletes shows that:
   - in the 100 m sprint, males are about 5% faster
   - in the marathon, males are about 10% faster
   - in the long jump, males jump nearly 16% further.

   a Why do males do better in running events than females?
   b Why is the difference bigger for the marathon than for the 100 m sprint?
   c Why can male long jumpers jump further?

12 At high altitudes the air is less dense than at low altitudes. It is thinner and lighter, and there is less oxygen in each litre of air.
  a What does *high altitude* mean? Give an example.
  b How would the thinner air affect an athlete's breathing?
  c Distance runners perform less well at high altitudes than at low altitudes. Why do you think this is?
  d 100 m sprinters often perform better at high altitudes than at low altitudes. Why is this?
  e Shot putters also perform better at high altitudes. Why do you think this is?
  f To compete in events at high altitudes, athletes train at high altitudes for about a month in advance. Why is this?

13 The three body types are:
  A endomorph
  B mesomorph
  C ectomorph
  Match each description below to A, B or C.

  i plump and pear-shaped
  ii broad muscular shoulders and narrow hips
  iii thin narrow chest and shoulders

14 A person's somatotype rating is given as 1 6 3.
  a What would you expect this person to look like?
  b Which of these sports would the person suit best?
    wrestling   long jump   gymnastics

15 Match each somatotype rating to the most suitable sport. You can choose a sport only once.

  A shot putting
  B basketball
  C wrestling
  D cycling

  i 6 5 2
  ii 2 4 3
  iii 4 6 3
  iv 2 5 4

16 Co-ordination is a skills-related aspect of fitness.
  a Why is it called *skills-related*?
  b Name two sports where good co-ordination is important.
  c Juggling needs good co-ordination. Make up a test to test co-ordination, using three tennis balls. Write clear instructions for the test.
  d Try the test out on your classmates.

Activities to try

Try these activities. You will need to work with a partner. For each activity:
  a record your score
  b say which aspect of fitness is being tested. (There may be more than one.)
  c name two sports where this aspect of fitness is very important
  d give two examples of how this aspect of fitness is needed in everyday life.

A Stand on one foot with your eyes closed. Time how long you can balance. Record the best score of two attempts.

B Hold your arm straight in front of you. Count how many times you can tightly clench and unclench your fist in 30 seconds. Only one attempt allowed.

C Your partner stands 1 metre behind you and throws a tennis ball over your shoulder without warning. Count how often out of ten attempts you can catch the ball before it bounces twice.

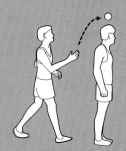

D Use chalk to mark out two lines 5 m long and 1 m apart. Place cones as shown. Time how long it takes to run in and out between all the cones. Record the best time of two attempts.

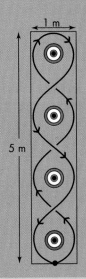

7.1 The principles of training

You want to get fitter or improve at your sport? **Training** is the answer. Training is a programme of exercise to help you reach your fitness goals. It is based on these four ideas or **principles**.

1 The principle of specificity

Every exercise has a **specific effect** on your body. For example a biceps curl with a heavy weight will strengthen your arm muscles. One with a light weight will improve their endurance. But neither will affect your leg muscles at all.

This means you must first decide what you want to improve, and then choose the right exercises. To improve in a sport, you must exercise the muscles and joints you use in the sport, and at the speed you use them. A training programme must be designed to suit *you*.

2 The principle of overload

To improve the fitness of a part of the body, you need to **overload** it. That means you need to make it work harder than usual. Over time, it adapts to meet the increased demand by getting fitter.

You can overload your body in three ways:

- by increasing the **frequency** of exercise – how often you do it.
  For example start by exercising twice a week, then move up to three or four times.
- by increasing the **intensity** of the exercise – how hard you work.
  For example run faster or lift heavier weights.
- by increasing the **time** you spend on exercise. If you are very unfit you might start off jogging just for 5 minutes a session, and work up week by week to 30 minutes a session.

A football team in training. A good footballer must have speed and agility, so shuttle runs and sprinting are included.

Both students are exercising their muscles, but the end results will be different. Heavy loads will build strength, many repetitions of light loads will improve endurance.

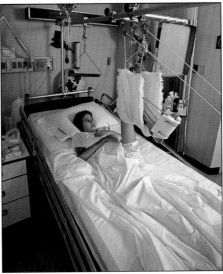

Here today, gone tomorrow. Strength training enlarges your muscles. That's called **hypertrophy**. But if you're confined to bed they waste away. That's **atrophy**.

3 The principle of progression

Your body takes time to adapt to increased demands on it. So you should build up your exercise level gradually or **progressively**. Otherwise you risk torn muscles and other injuries.

You will notice the biggest changes early in your training programme. The fitter you get, the harder it is to gain further improvement. This shows you are getting close to your full potential. If you keep exercising at a *constant* level your fitness will stay at that level.

4 The principle of reversibility

Sadly, improvements in fitness are **reversible**. Exercise harder and your body gets fitter. Stop exercising and it loses its fitness again.

It takes only three or four weeks to get out of condition. You lose endurance, strength, flexibility and speed. You rapidly get worse at things like jogging and swimming because your muscles get poorer at using oxygen. Muscles that are not used will waste away or **atrophy**.

Overtraining?

Training makes you fitter. But **overtraining** can make you ill. It causes soreness, joint pains, sleeping problems, loss of appetite and feelings of anxiety and great tiredness. You catch colds and flu more easily. These are signs you should cut down or take a break. The secret of good training is to take it gently.

Questions

1 The effects of training are *specific*. What does that mean?
2 What does *overloading* your body mean?
3 Describe three ways you could overload your body in a cycling training programme.
4 You should build up your exercise level gradually.
  a Why? b What is this principle called?
5 Write down four signs of overtraining.
6 'If it hurts it must be working'. Do you think this statement is true for training? Explain.

7.2 Training the energy systems

Your muscles use two kinds of energy system, **aerobic** and **anaerobic.** Which are they using right now?

Aerobic or anaerobic?

Most of the time your muscles work **aerobically**. That means they use oxygen for energy. But during all-out effort (as in the 100 m sprint) they work **anaerobically**. They don't use oxygen, but they produce lactic acid which tires them quickly.

Most sports are a mixture of aerobic and anaerobic work. You may use all-out effort during a tennis volley (anaerobic work) and then slow down again (aerobic work).

Training makes both energy systems work better. But the training is different for each. So you must study your sport to see how much of each system you use. Then decide on the best mix of training.

Training and heart rate

The harder you exercise, the faster your heart beats.
So heart rate is an indicator of how hard you are working and which energy system you are using.

The fastest your heart *can* beat is called your **maximum heart rate**. You can find it using this formula:

maximum heart rate = 220 – your age

At fifteen your maximum heart rate is 205 beats per minute (bpm).

You can measure your *actual* rate by taking your pulse. If it is around 60% of the maximum (say 120 bpm) you are working aerobically. If it is around 90% (185 bpm) you are probably working anaerobically.

Heart rate and training thresholds

To gain aerobic fitness:

- you must exercise **above** a minimum heart rate. This minimum rate depends on how fit you are. For an unfit fifteen-year-old it is about 120 bpm. Exercise below this will bring *no aerobic benefits*.
- you must also exercise *below* an upper limit. Once your heart rate rises above a certain point you are doing anaerobic work.
  You must exercise below this point to gain aerobic benefits.

This means that for aerobic training you must work within a range of heart rates. This is called your **aerobic training zone**. You reach it, and stay in it, by adjusting the intensity of your exercise.

The heart rates at the limits of the zone are called the **training thresholds**. The lower limit is the **aerobic threshold**. The upper limit is the **anaerobic threshold**.

When those leg muscles need energy for the really big push, anaerobic respiration takes over. Do you think they're working anaerobically here? What clues can you find?

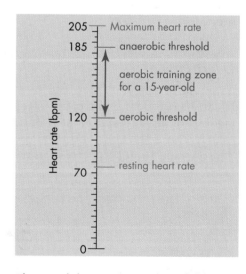

The aerobic training zone and the training thresholds. Where will the *anaerobic* training zone be?

78

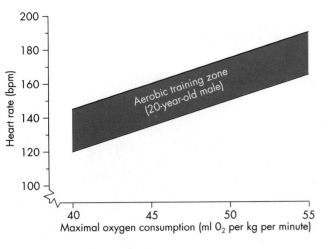

The fitter you are, the higher your training thresholds.

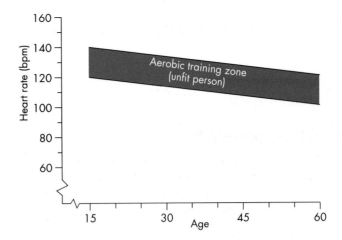

The older you are when you take up fitness training, the lower your aerobic training threshold is likely to be.

Aerobic training

- Choose an activity which involves the large muscles of the body and where you can work rhythmically for a long time.
  For example walking, swimming, jogging, cycling or skipping.
- Work for *at least* 15 to 20 minutes a session.
- Your heart rate should be within your aerobic training zone.
  This means it should be *at least* 60 % of your maximum heart rate. As you get fitter you can move up to 75% or so.
- Train *at least* three times a week. Otherwise it will not be effective.

Effects of aerobic training

- heart grows larger
- blood volume increases
- more capillaries grow
- fat burned more readily

See page 88 for more.

Anaerobic training

Anaerobic exercise puts a lot of stress on your heart and circulatory system. This means it can be dangerous. If you are unfit, do several weeks of aerobic training *before* you start on anaerobic training.

For anaerobic training:

- Use all-out effort for any of the above activities (running, swimming, cycling and so on).
- Take turns using all-out effort and lighter effort or rest, so that your body has time to pay off the oxygen debt and remove lactic acid.

You can find out more about energy training methods in the next Unit.

Effects of anaerobic training

- heart walls grow thicker
- muscles tolerate lactic acid better

See page 89 for more.

Questions

1 Name the two kinds of energy system your muscles use. What is the difference between them?

2 Describe how you could use both energy systems in a sport. (Not tennis!)

3 a What is *maximum heart rate*?
   b What it its value for a person aged 30?

4 a What does *aerobic training zone* mean?
   b Roughly what is *your* aerobic training zone?

5 What is *the aerobic threshold*?

6 What is *the anaerobic threshold*?

7 For anaerobic training you must work above the aerobic training zone. Explain why.

7.3 Methods of energy training

Continuous training

Continuous training is a good way to improve your aerobic system. It is also a good way to burn body fat. You run, swim, cycle or walk for at least thirty minutes at the same pace, without rest.
You overload by increasing the time, distance, speed or all three.

- Build up the time slowly, if you are unfit.
- Work in your aerobic training zone. Start at around 60% of your maximum heart rate and work up to 75%.
- If you are training for competitions, work up to distances that are 2 - 5 times the competition distance.

Continuous training has some disadvantages:

- It includes no skill work.
- It can get boring.
- If you are running to help improve your football game, for example, you will also need sprint sessions.

Continuous training improves your aerobic endurance – and tests your mental endurance. You need good motivation to keep going.

Fartlek training

Fartlek training was developed in Sweden. The word means *speed play*, and the method involves many changes of speed. You can use it to improve both aerobic and anaerobic energy systems. You can adapt it for running, cycling, skiing and other activities.

This is a typical 30-minute Fartlek running session:

Jog	5 min
Fast walk	3 min
Fast run with 50 m sprints every 200 m	5 min
Jog	3 min
Even run with 10 fast strides every 200 m	4 min
Uphill jog with 10 fast strides every minute	5 min
Fast skipping	3 min
Jog on the spot with high knee lifts	2 min

- Fartlek running sessions are very good for games players, since games have many changes of speed.
- Change the mix of fast and slow work to suit your sport and the energy system you want to work on.
- To overload, increase the time or speed for each activity or choose more difficult ground. For example run uphill or through sand.

Fartlek training has some disadvantages:

- The athlete decides on the speed. Coaches can't tell if athletes are working as hard as they should.
- It needs a lot of motivation to work at maximum speed, so it is easy to drop the effort.

Skipping is one way to add variety to a Fartlek training session.

Interval training

In **interval training** you follow a fixed pattern of fast work followed by slow work or rest. A session to improve acceleration at the start of a sprint race might go like this:

> A 30-metre sprint then 30 seconds of easy jogging.
> Repeat that 10 times. (10 repetitions or **reps**.)
> This completes one set. (A **set** is made up of a number of reps.)
>
> Then take a 2-minute rest.
>
> Do 3 sets altogether, with 2-minute rests in between.

The jogging is to help remove lactic acid. The 2-minute rest is to allow full recovery. You can tell by your heart rate if you have recovered. As you get fitter you can overload by:

- increasing the number of reps or sets or both
- reducing the time for slow work
- reducing the rest time between sets.

There is no point increasing the distance, since you are practicing acceleration. By about 30 metres you are already at full running speed.

Note these things about interval training:

- You can use it for either anaerobic or aerobic work, depending on the distance and the number and length of the intervals.
- You can use it for other activities such as cycling and swimming.
- It does cause pain so you need high motivation to keep going.
- Since there is a set pattern it is easy to tell if someone is giving up.

Aerobics

Aerobics classes are a popular way to improve aerobic fitness. You do exercises for every part of the body. You work at a pace that keeps your heart rate in the aerobic training zone.

- You work in time to music, which makes it fun.
- Jumping and stamping can jar your bones and damage your joints. To avoid this, work on a sprung hardwood floor or soft mat. Or else choose **low impact** aerobics. What do you think these are?

Aerobics classes make exercise fun.
(But isn't it always?)

Questions

1 What is *continuous training*? What activities could you use?
2 Name one disadvantage of continuous training.
3 What is *Fartlek training*?
4 Why is Fartlek training good for games players?
5 Make up a Fartlek training session for a cyclist.
6 What is *interval training*?
7 What is: **a** a rep? **b** a set?
8 Make up an interval training session for a swimmer who wants to do more anaerobic work.
9 Two of these training methods will *not* improve your anaerobic energy system. Which are they?

7.4 Types of muscle training

Here are three different ways to train muscles, based on different kinds of muscle contraction. All involve pulling or pushing or lifting a load.

Isotonic training

To bend your arm at the elbow, your biceps muscle shortens. This is called an **isotonic contraction**. All your body movements depend on isotonic contractions, when muscles shorten and pull on bones.

In **isotonic training** you use isotonic contractions to improve your muscle strength and endurance. Press-ups, sit-ups, chins and weight lifting are isotonic exercises. Can you think of others?

 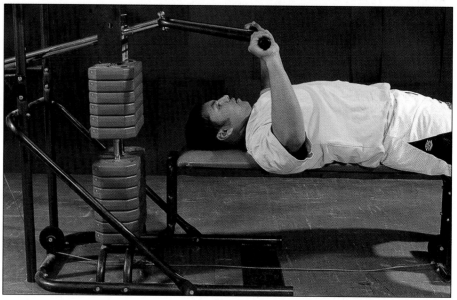

Advantages of isotonic training
- It strengthens a muscle through the full range of movement.
- You can choose isotonic exercises to suit your sport.

Disadvantages
- It can make muscles sore. This is caused by stress on muscles while they lengthen. For example there is stress on your arm muscles when you lower your body during chins.
- You gain most muscle strength at the weakest point of the action. You don't gain it evenly throughout.

They're both isotonic exercises, since muscles are contracting. But which muscles? And what's the advantage of the machine?

Isometric training

When you push against a closed door, your arm muscles contract but stay the same length. This is called an **isometric contraction**.

Isometric contractions produce **static strength**. This is the strength you need to push or pull a very heavy object or hold up a heavy load. You need it in sumo wrestling, a rugby scrum, gymnastics and weight lifting. **Isometric training** uses isometric contractions to strengthen your muscles. It can help for these sports.

82

These are isometric exercises: the length of the arm muscles isn't changing. But strength is gained *only* at the angle used in the exercise.

Advantages of isometric training
- It is quick to do and does not hurt.
- It does not need expensive equipment.
- You can do it anywhere.

Disadvantages
- A muscle gains strength *only* at the angle you use in the exercise. This might not help much in your sport.
- During isometric exercise, the blood flow to the muscle stops, blood pressure rises, and less blood flows back to the heart. This could be dangerous if you have heart problems.

Isometric training is best if you combine it with isotonic training.

Isokinetic training

In an **isokinetic contraction** your muscle contracts at constant speed. This does not happen during press-ups or other isotonic exercises. In these, muscles are always slower at the weak point in the action, which is usually at the start.

So for **isokinetic training** you need special machinery. It detects when a muscle is speeding up and increases the load to slow it down again.

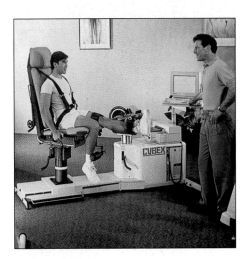

An isokinetic training machine.

Advantages of isokinetic training
- You gain strength equally all through the range of movement.
- You gain strength much faster than with other training methods.

A disadvantage
- The equipment is very expensive so not many gyms can afford it.

Questions

1 What is an *isotonic* contraction?
2 What is an *isometric* contraction?
3 What kind of contraction do you use when you:
  a run? b pull on the rope in a tug of war?
4 Give two advantages of isotonic training.
5 Name two isotonic exercises *not* mentioned here.
6 Who might benefit from isometric training?
7 Give two advantages of isometric training.
8 What is *isokinetic* training?
9 Give one big disadvantage of isokinetic training.

7.5 Methods of muscle training

For all sports you need a mixture of muscle strength and endurance:
- **strength** is the force your muscles exert when they contract.
- **endurance** is the ability of your muscles to maintain or repeat a contraction without getting tired.

How training changes your muscles

Strength training makes your muscles grow thicker. This makes the contractions stronger.

Endurance training does not make muscles thicker. But it makes them better at using oxygen and at burning fat for energy. It makes more capillaries grow around the muscles. So more oxygen reaches the muscles and they can work for longer.

Strength or endurance ?

All muscle training involves lifting or pulling or pushing a **load** or **resistance**. The load could be a dumb-bell, or your own body weight. You can use the same exercise to improve strength *or* endurance. It depends on the load and how often you repeat the exercise.

- For **endurance**, use a lighter load and many repetitions.
- For **strength**, use a heavy load and a small number of repetitions.

Training for different kinds of strength

There are three different kinds of strength. You can train for all three:

Static strength is the strength you need to push or pull a very heavy object, or to hold a heavy weight above your head.

Dynamic strength is the strength you need to keep a load moving over a long period of time. For example, for rowing or swimming.

Explosive strength or **power** is the strength you need for a single explosive act, such as a high jump or whacking a ball.

- Holding a heavy load stationary will improve your static strength.
- Moving it will improve your dynamic strength.
- Moving it as fast as possible will improve your power.

maximum load you can lift
twice without resting

maximum load you can lift
ten times without resting

short-term endurance
eg for gymnasts

medium-term endurance
eg for football

long-term endurance
eg for marathon

maximum load you can
lift one hundred times
without resting

For strength: higher loads, lower reps
For power: lift faster

For endurance: lower loads, higher reps

What size and type of load?

- You can use free weights such as dumb-bells, or weight training machines. This is called **weight training**. The diagram above shows how weights and reps should be matched to the type of fitness you want to improve. The RM number is the number of times you can lift a load without stopping for a rest.
- You can use your own **body weight**. For example in press-ups, sit-ups, dips and chins.
- You can use **resistance training**, where you exercise against a resistance. For example do the long-jump with weights attached to you, or run with a rope around your waist, dragging a tyre behind. This will improve muscular endurance.
- For muscle training to have an effect, you need *at least* three sessions a week.

More about weight training

Weight training is a popular way to exercise muscles.

- It is easy to tell what load you are using, since weights are clearly marked.
- It is easy to increase the load by the right amount.
- It is easy to work on different muscle groups, to suit your sport.
- But weight training is *not suitable* for people under sixteen. Your frame is still immature and you can get injured easily.

More about using your body weight

You do not need special equipment for body weight training. That means you can do it anywhere.

- When you can do an exercise such as press-ups more than 10 times without stopping, you are moving into endurance work.
- There are several ways to overload. For example with press-ups:
  - ask a partner to press on your upper back to increase the load.
  - put your feet on a bench to increase the load on your arms.

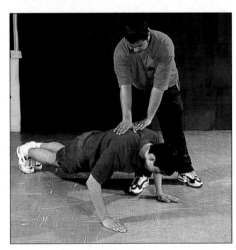

Two ways of overloading using body weight. Which muscles are being overloaded?

Questions

1 What is : **a** strength? **b** endurance?
2 How does strength training change your muscles?
3 How does endurance training change them?
4 Which of the two is improved by:
   a high load, low reps? **b** low load, high reps?

5 There are three different kinds of strength. What are they? Say how you could improve each.
6 Give two advantages of weight training.
7 Think of two advantages of body weight training.
8 How can you overload in body weight training?

7.6 Circuit training

Circuit training is a good way to organise your muscle training. A circuit usually has 8 to 15 **stations**. You do a different exercise at each station. This is a typical body weight circuit.

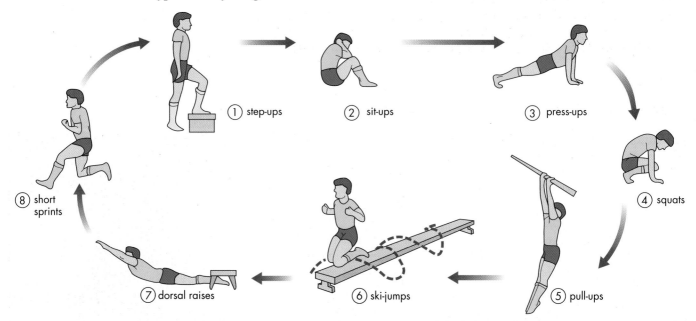

(1) step-ups (2) sit-ups (3) press-ups (4) squats (5) pull-ups (6) ski-jumps (7) dorsal raises (8) short sprints

There are several ways to go round the circuit. For example:

- Do a certain number of reps at each station, and time yourself for the whole circuit. Then try to improve the time in the next attempt.
- Or spend 1 minute at each station and do as many reps as you can.
- Do the circuit once, or several times with 2-minute rests in between.

Designing a circuit There is plenty of choice with a circuit. You can design one to improve strength, or endurance, or both. You can include weights. Many repetitions will also improve aerobic endurance. Fast intense work will improve anaerobic endurance.

- Decide what you want to improve, and which muscle groups.
- Choose exercises to give the effect you want.
- Include exercises for opposing muscle groups so that the strength around a joint is balanced. For example hamstrings *and* quadriceps.
- Switch muscle groups from station to station, to avoid fatigue.

Skills training Circuits can also be used to improve your skills for a sport. You practice a skill at each station. For example passing, dribbling and shuttle runs for football.

One disadvantage of circuit training is that it can take up a lot of space. It also needs good planning to stop the circuit getting too crowded.

Pressure training

- **Pressure training** is where you are put under pressure, during training.
- It usually means you have to complete a training task in a very short time, or train in a difficult situation.
- For example, suppose you are doing skills training as a goalkeeper. Shots are taken very quickly, one after the other and from different directions, to put you under pressure.
- Pressure training sharpens up your reactions.

Questions

1 What is *circuit training*?
2 What are the advantages of circuit training? Think of as many as you can.
3 Why should you include exercises for opposing muscle groups?
4 Suggest how to overload, in the circuit above.

7.7 Improving flexibility

Flexibility is the range of movement at a joint. Good flexibility is important in many sports. For example:

- flexible shoulders help you play tennis better.
- flexible hip, knee and ankle joints help you sprint. Your stride is longer so you cover the ground faster.
- a flexible spine helps divers and gymnasts move more smoothly.

Stretching

You improve **flexibility** through **static stretching**.

In static stretching, a muscle is held in a stretched position for a number of seconds. This can be done actively or passively.

In **active stretching,** you do the work. Don't jerk or bounce. Only stretch as far as is comfortable.

In **passive stretching** your partner does the work, holding you in a stretch for several seconds. Be careful. Too much force can injure you.

What happens at a joint when you stretch?

The joint capsule controls around half the movement at a joint. The rest depends mainly on muscles and tendons. When you stretch, your muscles and tendons get stretched. This makes them more flexible so the joint can move more freely.

A flexible joint is at less risk of strain. So stretching is part of the warm up for every training session. Flexibility is also linked to **strength**. Muscles that are stretched well can contract more strongly.

Questions

1 Try to think of two other examples (not used here) where flexibility helps in sport.
2 What kind of exercises will improve flexibility?
3 What is: **a** static stretching? **b** active stretching? **c** passive stretching?
4 How could passive stretching injure you?

7.8 The effects of training

Months of training can make big changes in your body. You met most of those changes earlier. We summarise them here.

The effects of aerobic training

1 On the heart and circulation Over months of swimming or jogging or cycling these changes take place:

- Your heart grows bigger. It holds more blood and contracts more strongly. More blood gets pumped out with each heart beat. Your heart becomes a more efficient pump.

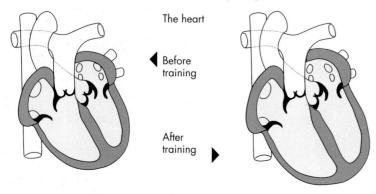

- Your resting heart rate falls, because now you can supply the same amount of blood with fewer heart beats. The fitter you are, the lower your resting heart rate.
- After exercise, your heart rate returns to its normal resting rate faster than it did before.
- The volume of blood in your body increases. You produce more red cells and more haemoglobin to help with oxygen delivery.
- Arteries grow larger and more elastic so blood pressure falls.

2 On the respiratory system Aerobic training also increases the fitness of your lungs and respiratory system.

- The rib muscles and diaphragm grow stronger. So the chest cavity gets bigger when you breathe in. This means the lungs can expand further, taking in more air with each breath.
- Since the lungs expand further, more alveoli are available for gas exchange. So more oxygen is picked up at each breath and more carbon dioxide removed.
- More capillaries grow around the alveoli, which means more blood gets carried to them.

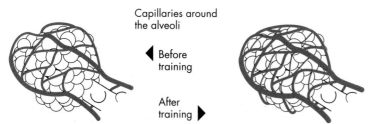

- This means you can move oxygen to the muscles faster and get rid of carbon dioxide faster. So you don't get tired so fast.

This champion swimmer has a larger heart, more blood, more capillaries, and a greater lung capacity than he had when he started training.

The effects of anaerobic training

Anaerobic training has these effects:

- Your heart walls get thicker to cope with the strain of all-out effort on your circulation system (especially the left ventricle wall).
- Your muscles are able to tolerate lactic acid better and clear it away faster. So you can go all out for longer than before.

The effects of muscle training

Endurance training Endurance training has these effects on muscles:

- They get better at using oxygen. So they can work harder for longer without fatigue.
- They get better at using fat for energy. This is good since your body has lots of stored fat! Fat gives more energy than glycogen per gram.
- More capillaries grow around the muscles so more blood reaches them, bringing oxygen and food and removing carbon dioxide.

Strength training Strength training has these effects on muscles:

- They grow thicker, because the muscle fibres grow thicker.
  An increase in muscle size and strength is called **hypertrophy**.
- They contract more strongly and efficiently.
- The tendons get bigger and stronger.

The effect on bones

As you saw on page 14, bones are alive. Cells called **osteoblasts** build new bone while cells called **osteoclasts** break it down again.
All training put extra stress on your bones. This makes the osteoblasts work harder so your bones get stronger.

The effects on joints

- Exercise makes ligaments stronger.
- It also thickens the cartilage at joints, so bones are better at absorbing shock.
- Stretching increases the range of movement at a joint, and helps muscles contract more strongly.

The effects on body fat

- Training increases your **basal metabolic rate**. You burn up stored fat faster even when you are resting.
- Since your muscles get better at using fat for energy, more fat is burned up during exercise too. So you get slimmer.

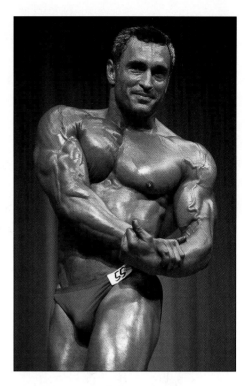

Endurance training has no effect on the size of your muscles. It takes strength training with heavy weights to develop them like this.

Questions

1 How would you expect these to change over months of jogging?
   a your resting heart rate   b your lung volume
   c your rib muscles   d your leg bones
   e the cartilage at your knee joints

2 It takes all-out effort to lift heavy weights. So the muscles work anaerobically. What effect will this have on the weightlifter's heart?

3 Training reduces body fat in two ways. What are they?

Questions on Chapter 7

1 Match each statement below to the correct letter A, B, C or D.

   A progression
   B overload
   C reversibility
   D specificity

   i   Weight training will thicken your muscle fibres.
   ii If you stop aerobic training your muscles quickly lose their improved ability to use oxygen.
   iii Gradually increase the weights you lift, week by week.
   iv You improve your fitness by increasing the demands you make on your body.

2 Is the statement true or false?
   a Anaerobic training makes your lungs expand.
   b Running improves the endurance of your leg muscles.
   c You could use the Fartlek method for weight lifting.
   d You must exercise at below 60% of your maximum heart rate to gain aerobic benefits.
   e You could use interval training for muscle strength.
   f Your maximum heart rate is the highest rate it reaches during a training session.
   g Your heart rate is not affected by anaerobic exercise.
   h Cycling strengthens your diaphragm.
   i Continuous training is also called long slow distance training.
   j Endurance training does not make your muscles thicker.

3 Say whether it is an isotonic or an isometric activity. Or could it be a mixture of the two?
   a running
   b holding a 50 kg bar bell steady at shoulder height
   c doing a handstand and holding it
   d cycling
   e arm wrestling with a friend
   f putting on your clothes in the morning
   g pushing a car that has run out of petrol
   h rock climbing
   i hanging from a beam

4 a Fartlek training
   b interval training
   c aerobics class
   d continuous training
   e body weight circuit

For each of these training methods:
   i   name one advantage
   ii name one disadvantage
   iii say what kind(s) of fitness it will improve. (There may be more than one.)

5 Which of the training methods in Exercise 4 would you include in your training for:
   a running a marathon?
   b a 100 m swim race?
   c the rugby season?
   d gymnastics?
   e the Tour de France?
   f rock climbing?
You can choose more than one method if you wish. Explain your answers.

6 For each of these activities:
   a say what kind of fitness is being improved
   b name two effects it will have on your body
   c name two sports where it will help you
   d say how you could overload

7 This graph shows how a healthy fifteen-year-old's heart rate changed during a training run.

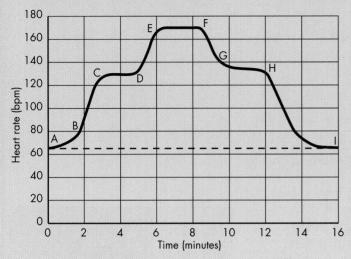

a Is she fit or unfit? Explain why you think so.
b What do you think she was doing between A and B?
c Between what points was she jogging at an easy pace?
d At what point did she speed up in her run?
e Would you say she was working anaerobically at any point? Explain your answer.

8 This shows an athlete's heart before and after a six-month training programme.

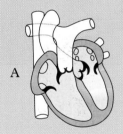 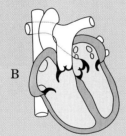

a Which drawing shows the heart *after* training?
b What kind of training would produce this effect? Name two suitable training activities.
c What effect did training have on this athlete's:
 i stroke volume? ii heart rate?
 Explain why these effects occurred.
d Name four further changes you would expect to see in this athlete's body.

9 Is this affected by *anaerobic* training?
 If yes, explain what the effect will be.
 a your bone strength
 b how long you can continue with all-out effort
 c how quickly you can clear away lactic acid from your body after hard exercise
 d the amount of haemoglobin in your blood
 e the volume of oxygen your lungs can take in
 f the cartilage at the ends of your bones
 g the strength of your ligaments

Things to do

Estimating your heart rate

You can get a good idea of your heart rate from how hard you *feel* you are working. This is called **perceived exertion**.

The table below shows feelings on a scale from 6 to 20. You find your estimated heart rate by multiplying the rating by 10. For example if an exercise feels very very light its rating is 7. Your estimated heart rate is therefore $7 \times 10 = 70$.

How the exercise feels	Rating
	6
Very very light	7
	8
Very light	9
	10
Fairly light	11
	12
Somewhat hard	13
	14
Hard	15
	16
Very hard	17
	18
Very very hard	19
	20

a Do 3 minutes of what you feel is very very light activity (rating 7). For example it could be gently swinging your arms. Now measure your pulse for 10 seconds. What is your heart rate in beats per minute? How close is it to 70?

b Now do 3 minutes of what feels like hard activity (rating 15). For example it could be running hard on the spot, raising your knees as high as you can. Take your pulse immediately for 10 seconds. What is your heart rate in bpm? How close is it to 150?

c Repeat for different activities until your feelings match the heart rate scale.

An isometric exercise

a Sit against the wall in this position. Time how long you can stay this way. The pain shows that lactic acid has built up. So your leg muscles are working even though you are still.

b Repeat three times a week for the next three weeks. What do you notice?

8.1 Planning a training programme

Planning a training programme for yourself or someone else?
These are the steps.

1 Find out about the person it's for

Suppose it's for a female called Jane. It will work well only if it suits her needs. So find out these things about her:

- **her age**. A programme that suits a a person of twenty could harm a person of fourteen.
- **her current level of health**. If she has just recovered from a long illness, for example, you need to take that into account.
- **her current level of fitness**. Does she exercise already? Is she generally fit? Is she overweight or overfat? Tests could help here.
- **why she wants to get fitter**. Does she just want to feel healthier? Or to improve her skills in a sport?
- **what kind of exercise she enjoys**. If she likes your programme she is more likely to stick with it.

2 Analyse the person's needs

Hi, I'm Jane.

> Jane - 16 years old.
> No exercise for months.
> Overfat. Wants to lose weight.
> Has already started to eat less.
> Likes swimming. Lives near a pool.
> Hates jogging.
> Later this year she would like to take up tennis.

An aerobic fitness programme is the best start for Jane, because:
- it will make her both fitter and healthier.
- it will help her slim since aerobic exercise burns up body fat.
- it will help her when she takes up tennis. Aerobic fitness is a good basis for all sports.

3 Plan the programme

Now it's time to plan the training programme. Think of the word **FITT**:

F = frequency
I = intensity
T = time
T = training activity

Training activity Let's start with the training activity. This is what you will ask Jane to do. It should be something:

- that will improve her aerobic fitness
- that will be safe and convenient for her, and that she'll enjoy

Swimming is a good choice. It is safe for unfit and overweight people because water supports the body and your bones don't jar.

Frequency Training should be at least 3 times a week to take effect. Jane feels three times a week is enough for her.

Intensity It is important to start at the right intensity.

- If a programme is too demanding, muscles get sore and strained. This puts the person off. It is better to start too low than too high.
- Jane should start at around 60% of her maximum heart rate. Why?
- How Jane feels is also a good guide. If she feels it is easy, raise the intensity until she finds it difficult *but still manageable*.

Time For training to take effect, a person needs to spend:

- at least 20 minutes for an aerobic training session
- at least 15 minutes for a muscle training session
- at least four to six weeks to see real benefit.

(These times do not include warm up and cool down. See page 94!)

A suitable six-week programme for Jane

Week	Session	Swimming activity (minutes)
1	1	15 at easy pace.
	2	15 at a slightly faster pace.
	3	15 at a firm pace.
2	1	20 at easy pace.
	2	6 with arms only, then 6 with legs only, using float. Then 6 at easy pace.
	3	3 at easy pace, 3 at firm pace, 1 at fast pace. 3 reps.
3	1	25 at easy pace.
	2	7 with arms only, then 7 with legs only, using float. Then 7 at easy pace.
	3	3 at easy pace, 3 at firm pace, 2 at fast pace. 3 reps.
4	1	30 at easy pace.
	2	8 with arms only then 8 with legs only, using float. Then 8 at easy pace.
	3	3 at easy pace, 4 at firm pace, 3 at fast pace. 3 reps.
5	1	5 at easy pace, 5 at firm pace. 3 reps.
	2	9 with arms only, then 9 with legs only, using float. Then 9 at easy pace.
	3	2 at easy pace, 3 at firm pace, 1 at fast pace. 5 reps.
6	1	5 at easy pace, 10 at firm pace. 2 reps.
	2	10 with arms only, then 10 with legs only, using float. Then 10 at easy pace.
	3	1 at easy pace, 3 at firm pace, 2 at fast pace. 5 reps.

Questions

1 Why is aerobic exercise a good start, for an unfit person? Think of as many reasons as you can.

2 Suppose a 15-year-old wants to improve his football skills. Would you give him Jane's programme? Explain why.

3 What do the letters FITT stand for?

4 It helps if the person enjoys the training programme. Think of three reasons why.

5 a What is Jane's maximum heart rate? (page 78)
  b At around what heart rate should she train? Why?

6 What other guide to intensity could you use instead of her heart rate?

7 a What is the principle of overload? (page 76)
  b Does Jane's programme show it? Explain.

8 a What is the principle of progression?
  b Does Jane's programme show it? Explain.

8.2 The training session

Every training session should have three parts: the warm up, the training activity and the cool down.

1 The warm up

The **warm up** is light exercise to get you ready for the main activity. In cold weather wear a track suit and plenty of layers.

- Start with light jogging for a minute or two. This warms your muscles. It makes them more flexible and lowers the risk of injury. It increases your heart rate and blood flow. It warms the synovial fluid and makes your joints more mobile.
- Next do some stretching. Work all the main joints. Stretching increases the range of movement at the joints. It helps to stop muscles, tendons and ligaments getting strained. Hold each stretch for at least 10 seconds, with no bouncing.
- Now do a specific warm up for the activity. For example a few tennis serves or some netball shooting practice. As well as working your muscles, this helps to prepare you mentally.

By the end of the warm up you should be sweating lightly. Move on to the training activity as soon as possible.

2 The training activity

This is the body of the training session. It could be:

- continuous, fartlek or interval training for an aerobic activity
- an actual practice game, for example netball or football
- circuit training to develop muscle fitness or skill.

For example a typical skills training session for a cricketer would be:

Activity	Time (minutes)
batting	15
– working on the different shots, a few minutes on each – off-drives, on-drives, pulls and cuts	
fielding	15
– close catching, high catching, picking up and throwing	

3 The cool down

The **cool down** is where you help your body to recover after vigorous exercise. It is just as important as the warm up.

- Start with a few minutes of gentle exercise such as jogging. This helps to keep your circulation going. So more oxygen reaches your muscles and lactic acid is cleared away faster. This means less soreness.
- Finish with some stretching. This will help loosen your muscles and prevent stiffness. After heavy exercise muscles often get very tight.

Light jogging: a good start to the warm up for any training session, and a good way to cool down.

Stretch those muscles. As part of the warm up it helps to prevent injury. Do it in the cool down to stop soreness.

Recovery rate

Your **recovery rate** is how quickly your body gets back to normal after exercise. These are some of the changes that take place.

Heart rate. This slows down to your normal resting rate. How long that takes depends on how hard you exercise and how fit you are. The fitter you are the faster your heart rate returns to normal.

Lactic acid. Lactic acid is removed by oxygen when you repay the oxygen debt (page 41). It is removed faster when you do a cool down (active recovery), as the graph on the left below shows.

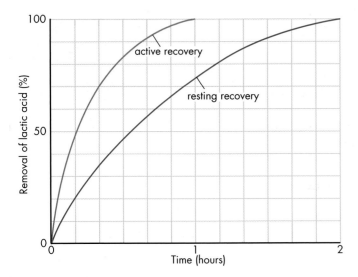

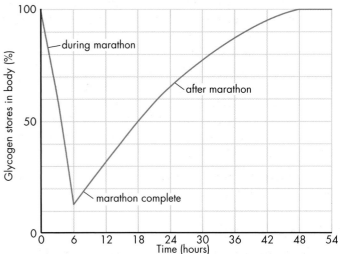

Glycogen stores. During exercise, muscle glycogen gets used up. It takes time to replace. After prolonged exercise such as marathon running, it can take 48 hours for glycogen stores to fully recover. Look at the graph on the right above.

Muscles. Your body has to repair any damage done to muscles during training. Stiffness and soreness take time to clear.

Recovery time

- Make sure you take enough time to recover between training sessions - 24 to 48 hours in the early stage of a training programme.
- If you train every day, follow a heavy session one day with a light session the next, to help recovery.
- Even during a heavy training period, take one rest day a week.

Questions

1 What are the three stages of a training session?
2 What should you do during a warm up?
3 Describe all the ways a warm up helps you.
4 What should you do during a cool down?
5 Describe all the ways a cool down helps you.
6 What is *recovery rate*?
7 If your heart rate returns to normal very quickly after hard exercise, what does that show?

8 Look at the first graph above.
a What does it show?
b How long does the process take:
  i without cool down? ii with cool down?
9 Now look at the second graph.
a Why does the glycogen level fall at the start?
b How long does it take to recover?
c What could the athlete do to speed up recovery?

8.3 The athlete's year

If you are a judo player, you can take part in judo events all year round. But many sports are **seasonal**. Cricket is an example. In the UK, cricket is played from May to September.

This shows how the year is divided for an athlete who plays a seasonal sport. The calendar is for a 'winter' sport such as netball or rugby. A cricket player will follow the same pattern but over different months, since cricket is a 'summer' sport.

June	July	Aug	Sept	Oct	Nov	Dec	Jan	Feb	Mar	April	May	June
	1 PREPARATION			2 COMPETITION							3 RECUPERATION	
	(i) out-of-season	(i) pre-season										

1 Preparation

i Out-of-season Here the athletes build up to a high level of general fitness. They do continuous training over long distances to improve aerobic fitness. They have strength training for the major muscle groups. They are careful with diet: lots of carbohydrate, not much fat!

This shows a typical out-of-season training programme for the England netball team.

Weekly programme for June/July	
Monday	4 - 5 mile run
Tuesday	Strength training using weights
Wednesday	3 - 4 mile run
Thursday	Strength training using weights
Friday	3 mile run
Saturday	Rest
Sunday	Strength training using weights

ii Pre-season Here the athletes focus on fitness for the sport. They run short fast lengths to improve anaerobic fitness and speed. They continue strength training on the muscles needed for the sport but work faster to improve their power.

Skills training becomes important, with circuits designed to practice different skills. For example footwork, shooting and defending in netball. Now is the time to really sharpen up.

Weekly programme for August/September	
Monday	Skills training including jumping (plyometrics)
Tuesday	3 mile run (Time it and aim to go faster next time.)
Wednesday	Strength/power training using weights
Thursday	Skills training including intense anaerobic work
Friday	Strength/power training using weights
Saturday	Fast 3 mile run
Sunday	Rest

2 Competition

Here the athletes play at least two matches a week. The aim is to win! They still need training to maintain fitness, and to build up to peak performance in the main event of the season. They need extra care to avoid injury at this time. It is easy to get injured through tiredness, or by overusing muscles.

Weekly programme for October	
Monday	Rest
Tuesday	Skills and weight training
Wednesday	Sprint or skills or plyometrics as necessary
Thursday	Fast 2 mile run, skills training
Friday	Strength/power training using weights
Saturday	Match
Sunday	Match

A happy and victorious England netball team.

Many important events are overseas, in hotter weather or at higher altitude. The athletes will travel in advance so that they can train under the right conditions for the match.

3 Recuperation

Time for rest and relaxation. The aim is complete recovery from the competition season. But the athletes do not laze around. They play other sports for exercise and enjoyment. They are still careful with diet so as not to put on extra weight. Lots of carbohydrate, not much fat.

Questions

1. Give three examples of: a seasonal sports
   b sports which are played all year round
2. For seasonal sports, the year has three main stages.
   a What are they?
   b What is the main purpose of each stage?

3. Look at the netballers' programme for June/July. What will be the effect of these activities?
4. The August/September programme includes some fast runs. Why?
5. What is a *skills training circuit*? Give an example.

1 A training programme designed to suit an individual is also called a personal exercise programme or PEP. To design a PEP for someone, you need to know:

a the person's age
b whether he or she has any health problems
c the person's present level of fitness
d why he or she wants to get fitter
e what kind of exercise he or she enjoys.

For each item, explain why you need to know it.

2 To design a training programme, you need to think of the word FITT. Explain what each letter stands for.

3 This shows the first six weeks of a personal exercise programme designed for a woman aged 50. She hasn't done any exercise for months, but likes walking.

Week	1	2	3	4	5	6
Frequency	2	3	3	3	3	3
Time (min)	20	30	40	38	36	34
Distance (km)	1.5	2.3	3.1	3.1	3.1	3.1

a What is the correct technical name for this training method?
b Is it aerobic or anaerobic?
c How often should the woman walk in week 2?
d From weeks 3 to 6, the frequency and distance don't change. Does this mean there is no progression? Explain.
e What is the woman's maximum heart rate?
f About what should her *minimum* heart rate be, during the walk, to ensure she is gaining aerobic benefit? (Hint: check on page 78.)

4 This is also about the personal exercise programme in question 3.

a The woman is doing the programme in early summer. Suggest suitable clothing and footwear.
b What advice would you give her about eating before exercise? Why is this important?
c Since her exercise is just walking, do you think the woman needs to do a warm up? Explain your answer.
d If your answer to c was yes, suggest what she should do for the warm up.
e Should she do a cool down? Explain your answer.
f If your answer to e was yes, suggest what she should do for the cool down.
g Suppose she is finding it all too easy by week 3. What changes would you suggest?
h What could she do to prevent boredom setting in? Suggest as many things as you can.

5 A training session to improve aerobic fitness could combine two or more activities, for example skipping and jogging. Do you think this is a good idea? Explain your answer.

6 This shows a six-week PEP designed for an unfit and slightly overweight 15-year-old who wants to get fitter before the summer holidays. Her resting pulse rate is 85.

Week 1	Mon	Jogging 5 min + skipping 3 min
	Thurs	Jogging 10 min + skipping 5 min
Week 2	Mon	Jogging 15 min + skipping 8 min
	Thurs	Jogging 20 min + skipping 10 min
Week 3	Mon	Jogging 25 min + skipping 12 min
	Wed	Jogging 30 min + skipping 14 min
	Fri	Jogging 35 min + skipping 16 min
Week 4	Mon	Jogging 40 min + skipping 18 min
	Wed	Jogging 45 min + skipping 20 min
	Fri	Jogging 50 min + skipping 22 min
Week 5	Mon	Jogging 55 min + skipping 24 min
	Wed	Jogging 60 min + skipping 26 min
	Fri	Jogging 65 min + skipping 28 min
Week 6	Mon	Jogging 70 min + skipping 30 min
	Tue	Jogging 70 min + skipping 32 min
	Thurs	Jogging 70 min + skipping 34 min
	Sat	Jogging 70 min + skipping 36 min

a What can you tell from her resting pulse rate?
b This a badly-designed programme. Explain why. Give as many reasons as you can.

7 Now redesign the programme in question 6 to make it more suitable for the girl.

8 Design a 6-week training programme for a 16-year-old footballer who plays a match on Saturdays and trains with his club on Wednesdays. He likes running and wants to be fitter for his sport.

9 You are about to play a tennis match.
a Name six muscles you will use a lot during the match.
b What is the advantage of warming up these muscles before you start?
c What will you do to warm up your muscles?
d You should include stretching exercises in your warm up session. Give two examples of how this will help you play a better game.
e From your own experience of warm ups, describe five stretching exercises you could do.

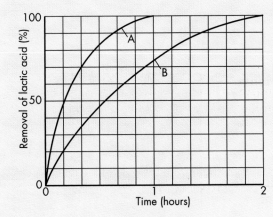

This graph shows time taken to clear lactic acid from the body after exercise.

a Why is it good to clear away lactic acid quickly?

b One curve shows the time it takes to clear the lactic acid when the athlete does a cool down. Which one?

c Name one other benefit of the cool down.

d Describe what activities you would do for a cool down, after a hard game of tennis.

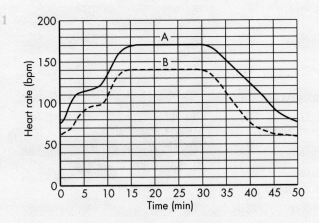

This graph show how the heart rates for two runners A and B changed during a run.

a Which runner was fitter? How can you tell?

b Did they do a warm up? Explain your answer.

12 a In training, what does *recovery rate* mean?

b Name four ways in which your body needs to recover after a hard training session.

c How long you take to recover after exercise depends on two main factors. What are these factors?

d If you train every day, you should follow a heavy session with light one. Why?

e How could you tell that an athlete was training *too* hard? (Hint: check on page 77.)

13 For seasonal training, the year is divided into these parts:

A Out-of-season + pre-season preparation
B Competition
C Recuperation
Explain the purpose of each part.

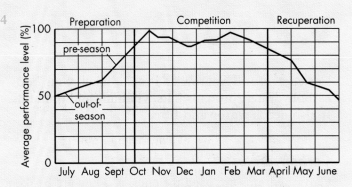

This graph how an athlete's level of performance changed through the year.

a Her performance level improved all through the preparation period. Explain why.

b It improved faster as she moved from out-of-season preparation to pre-season preparation. Why?

c The athlete **peaked** (hit her top performance level) twice in the competition season. When did this happen?

d There was a drop in performance in the second part of December. Why do you think this was?

e The athlete's main event took place at the end of March. Was she at her best then?

f Give reasons why an athlete's performance does not remain at its peak all through the competition season.

15 This shows a typical training programme for an 800 m male runner during pre-season preparation:

Monday	30 km road run
Tuesday	800 m on grass x 4 times, with a 3-minute rest between runs
Wednesday	8 km run followed by weight training for arms, shoulders and legs
Thursday	400 m run on track in around 62 secs. Repeat x 11 with a 2-minute rest between runs
Friday	45 minute Fartlek training
Saturday	10 km easy run followed by weight training for arms, shoulders and legs
Sunday	Rest day

a Give the correct name for the type of training he does:
 i on Mondays ii on Tuesdays and Thursdays

b What kind of fitness does the Monday session improve?

c What kind of fitness is improved on Thursdays?

d Give two examples of the type of activity he might do during Fartlek training.

e The programme includes weight training for arms and shoulders. How do you think that will help a runner?

f Would you expect him to use heavy, medium or light weights during weight training? Explain.

g The athlete does a different kind of training each day. In what two ways might this help him?

99

9.1 The foods your body needs

For energy, and to grow and repair itself, your body needs **nutrients**: carbohydrates, proteins, fats, vitamins and minerals.
It also needs **water** and **fibre**.

Carbohydrates

Carbohydrates are used for energy. They are broken down to **glucose** in your gut and used as a fuel for cell respiration (page 40). Some glucose is stored as **glycogen** in the liver and muscles.

Carbohydrates are found in sweet and starchy foods. Examples are bananas and other fruits, bread, biscuits, breakfast cereals, rice, potatoes and spaghetti.

These are just some of the foods that are rich in carbohydrates.

Fats

Fats are also used for energy. Muscles use a mixture of fats and glycogen. The mixture depends on how intense the exercise is, how long it lasts and how fit you are. For example:

- on a long walk, muscles use mainly fat
- start jogging and they'll start using more glycogen
- switch to a sprint and they'll use glycogen only
- jog for a few hours and they'll switch increasingly to fat, as glycogen gets used up
- the fitter you are, the more readily your muscles use fat in place of glycogen.

Butter, margarine, sunflower oil and other cooking oils are fats. Hamburgers, red meats, sausages, bacon, cheese and cream contain a lot of fat. So do oily fish, nuts and avocado pears.
Fats are used in making crisps, cakes and biscuits.

These are all rich in fats.

Protein

Your body needs proteins to build cells, to make blood, and to restore and repair muscle and other tissues. They are found in meat, liver, chicken, eggs, fish, beans, peas, lentils and nuts.

Your body can also use proteins for energy. But it will do this only if it has run out of carbohydrates and fats.

Vitamins and minerals

Your body needs tiny amounts of vitamins. Vitamins A and D can be stored in your liver. Vitamin C can't be stored. If you eat more of it than you need, the extra is excreted. That means you must eat it regularly.

Minerals are just as important as vitamins. There is enough iron inside you to make a large nail. Without iron your blood can't carry oxygen. Without calcium you'd have no bones, teeth or muscle contractions.

These are rich in protein.

Substance	Where you find it ...	Why you need it ...	A shortage leads to ...
vitamin A	fish, liver, vegetables, eggs, milk	to see in dim light and for healthy skin	night blindness and flaking skin
vitamin C	oranges and other citrus fruits, vegetables	for healthy skin and gums and to help wounds heal	scurvy
vitamin D	made by skin in sunshine; found in milk, fish, liver and eggs	for strong bones and teeth (you can't absorb calcium without it)	rickets
calcium	milk, cheese, dried fish, sardines, green vegetables	for strong bones and teeth, and for muscle contractions	fragile bones
iron	liver, beans, lentils, green vegetables; added to bread	for the haemoglobin in red blood cells	tiredness and anaemia
iodine	sea food and vegetables grown near the sea	for thyroid hormones that control the rate at which you burn up food for energy	a swollen thyroid gland (goitre)

Water

Water does not give you energy. But around half your weight is water. Some is in your blood and other body fluids. Most is in your body cells, where it plays a vital part in reactions.

You could last for several weeks without food, but only 4 or 5 days without water. Once the level in your blood and body fluids falls too low, water is drawn out from the cells. You die.

You should drink at least six glasses of water a day. If you play sports you may need to drink much more. Why?

Fibre

Fibre is a substance called **cellulose** from the cell walls of plants. You find it in fruit, vegetables, brown bread, bran and other cereals. You can't digest it. It passes straight through the gut and is excreted as faeces. But it is very important because:

- it makes a bulky mass which the muscles of your gut can grip and push along quickly. This prevents constipation and bowel cancer.
- it absorbs poisonous wastes from digested food.
- it makes you feel full, so you eat less.

These will provide you with plenty of fibre.

Questions

1 Your body needs five nutrients. Which are they?
2 a Which nutrient is found in all sweet foods?
  b What does your body use this nutrient for?
3 What does your body use fat for?
4 Why do you need protein?

5 Say why you need it and where you get it:
  a vitamin A b vitamin C c vitamin D
  d iron e calcium f iodine
6 Why is fibre good for you?
7 Name three foods that are rich in fibre.

9.2 A balanced diet

Your energy needs

Even when you are relaxed and resting you need energy.
You need it to keep you warm, to keep your heart beating and lungs breathing, and for all the reactions that go on in your cells.

- Your **basal metabolic rate** (BMR) is the amount of energy you need just to stay alive, awake and comfortably warm.
- To move around, digest food and do exercise, you need even more energy. This is called **working energy**. It depends on how active you are.
- **total energy needed = basal metabolic rate + working energy**
  It can be measured in **kilojoules** (kJ) or in **kilocalories** (C).
  1 kilocalorie = 4.18 kilojoules

Different people have different energy needs

Look at this table. It shows how different people have different energy needs. It depends on:

- **your age.** You need more energy now than when you were little.
- **your sex.** Males usually need more energy than females of the same age.
- **your lifestyle.** The more active you are, the more energy you need.

	Total energy needed in a day (kJ)	
	male	*female*
child aged 8	8200	7300
teenager aged 15	11 500	8800
adult doing office work	10 500	9000
adult doing heavy work	14 000	10 500
a retired person of 75	9000	7000

How much energy do foods give?

Your body can use carbohydrates, fats *and* proteins for energy.
Compare the energy each gives:

1 gram of carbohydrate	17.1 kJ
1 gram of protein	18.2 kJ
1 gram of fat	38.9 kJ

A gram of fat gives over twice as much energy as a gram of protein or carbohydrate. So it is very easy to eat much more fat than you need for energy. When this happens you put on weight!

Most foods are a mixture of carbohydrates, fats and proteins. Labels on tins and cartons often show what is in food and how much energy it will give you. Look at labels to find out what you are eating!

The energy balance

Suppose you need 10 000 kJ of energy a day. You eat enough food to give 15 000 kJ. This is much more than you need. But the extra food is not excreted. Instead *it is stored as fat*. Even carbohydrate and protein are changed into fat and stored.

- If energy in *is greater than* energy out, the extra food is stored as fat and you gain weight. If you gain too much you may become **obese**.
- If energy in = energy out, your weight will not change.

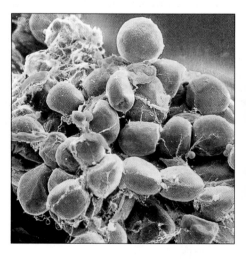

The yellow blobs are fat-storing cells, magnified by 150. Most of your fat-storing cells are laid down when you're a baby. When you eat more food than you need, they get bigger and you get fatter!

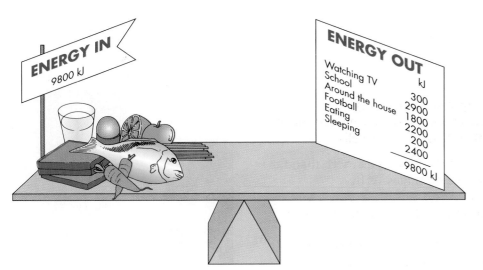

Energy in balance: if energy in = energy out you won't put on weight.

- If energy in *is less than* energy out, your body will use up stored body fat for the extra energy. You will grow slimmer. But if too much body fat gets used up you'll become **anorexic**.

A balanced diet

To be healthy you need a **balanced diet**. That means a diet that matches your energy needs *and* give the right mixture of nutrients and fibre. Here are some guidelines for you.

- Eat lots of fresh fruit and vegetables. They give you carbohydrates, fibre, vitamins and minerals.
- Eat starchy foods such as brown bread, pasta, potatoes and rice for carbohydrates and fibre.
- Eat fish, eggs and white meats for protein. But get at least some vegetable protein from beans, peas, nuts and lentils.
- Cut down on fatty foods. They make you fat and can cause heart disease and obesity. Beware of the hidden fats in chips, cakes, crisps and biscuits.
- Cut down on sugar. It is pure carbohydrate. It gives you energy but rots your teeth and is linked to heart disease. Beware of the hidden sugar in soft drinks, jams and sauces.
- Cut down on salt. Doctors think it can cause high blood pressure.
- Cut down on **processed foods** such as 'ready to cook' meals. In processing food, fibre and other goodness is removed. Sugar, salt and chemicals called **additives** are added for flavour and colour. None of these are good for you. They can be harmful.

15% protein

30% fat

55% carbohydrate

A balanced diet: around 15% protein, 30% fat and 55% carbohydrate. Not only are carbohydrates good for you, they are also comparatively cheap.

Questions

1 What is your *basal metabolic rate*?
2 Explain why a teenage male needs more energy than a retired female.
3 What two units are used to measure energy?

4 If you eat more food than you need for energy, what happens to the extra?
5 What is *a balanced diet*?
6 What is *processed* food? Why is fresh food better?

9.3 Weight control and fitness

Body weight

What weight are you? It will depend on:

- your height and frame size. The longer and thicker your bones the more you will weigh.
- how much muscle and fat you have. (Muscle weighs more than fat.)
- your sex. Males are usually heavier than females. Why?

Weight tables show what weight a person of your height *should* be. If you are more than this you are **overweight**. You have too much fat - or perhaps even too much muscle. More muscle than you need for your work or sport puts extra strain on the heart, joints and ligaments.

Ask your teacher for a weight chart if you would like to check your weight.

Fitness and body composition

You could be the right weight but very unfit. For example you could have lots of fat, and only small weak muscles. So **body composition** is a better indicator of fitness. It shows how much fat you have compared with muscle, bone and other tissue.

- If you are male, no more than 13 - 15 % of your weight should be fat. If it is more you are **overfat**. If it's over 20% you are **obese**.
- If you are female, no more than 18 - 20 % of your weight should be fat. If it is more you are overfat. If it's over 30% you are obese.

You need a certain amount of fat. It forms a protective cushion around the kidneys and other organs. The layer of fat under your skin keeps you warm and acts as a store of energy.

But **obesity** means you have an abnormal proportion of fat. If you are overfat or obese, the extra weight puts a strain on the heart, muscles, bones and ligaments. Exercise becomes difficult or even dangerous. Obesity causes joint and back injuries, and leads to heart attacks, strokes, liver disease and other problems.

Underweight?

You are **underweight** if you are below the normal weight range for your height. You could be underweight *and* overfat at the same time. Exercise will make you feel weak and tired.

Anorexia

Some people go on harsh diets to lose weight. This is very dangerous. It can lead to **anorexia**. You don't eat enough carbohydrate, so your body uses stored fat for energy. Then it runs out of fat and starts using proteins. It takes these proteins from your body tissues. So your organs stop working properly. You may die.

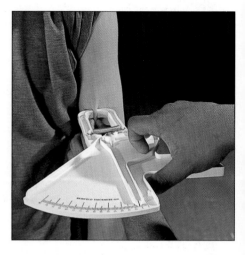

The skinfold test measures body fat. If you'd like to try it, ask your teacher.

If this young woman were anorexic, she'd see herself as horribly obese. People with anorexia have a distorted self-image. They need both medical and emotional help.

How to lose weight

The way to lose weight is by *combining* exercise and diet.

- Eat a healthy balanced diet, but less of it. And exercise more. Your body will use up stored fat to obtain the extra energy.
- Your muscles will grow when you exercise. Muscle weighs more than fat but takes up less space. So you won't lose much weight at the start but you will look slimmer.
- Regular exercise increases your basal metabolic rate. That means you use up more stored fat even when you are resting.
- Regular exercise reduces your appetite. You will find it easier to say no to food.

Eating for sport

The best food for sport is a healthy balanced diet.

- Don't eat more than you need. The extra will be stored as fat, and fat is a burden in sport.
- Carbohydrates will be your main source of energy. Remember, a balanced diet should contain at least 55% carbohydrate.
- You will also use fats for energy, depending on how intense the activity and how long it lasts. The more intense it is, the more you depend on carbohydrates. The longer it lasts, the more you depend on fats. But you don't need to eat extra fat. You have plenty stored.
- Intense exercise causes wear and tear to muscle and other tissue. Proteins are needed to repair the damage. But there's enough for that task in a normal diet. You don't need extra.
- Make sure you drink water during and after sport. Why?
- A balanced diet will give you enough vitamins and minerals. You do not need supplements. In fact an excess of vitamins A and D can be dangerous.

An athlete breakfasting before his big Olympic event. Plenty of carbohydrate!

Carboloading

For long events (two hours or more) athletes often use **carboloading**.

First, cut down on carbohydrates and train hard. This uses up all your glycogen. Then eat lots of carbohydrates and train lightly in the days just before the event. Your muscles will now store more glycogen than usual.

By a combination of diet and exercise, some athletes have stored up to four times more glycogen than usual. But this can cause problems. Muscles may feel stiff and heavy. Kidneys may not function properly. The athlete may suffer chest pains. So a steady diet of at least 55% carbohydrate is a better solution.

Questions

1 How can you tell if you are overweight?
2 What does *overfat* mean?
3 What is *obesity*? What problems does it cause?
4 A person can be underweight *and* overfat. Explain.

5 Why are harsh diets dangerous?
6 List three ways exercise helps you lose weight.
7 What is *carboloading*? How does it help athletes?
8 What's the best mix of main nutrients to eat?

9.4 Drugs and sport (1)

Drugs and doping

A **drug** is any chemical substance you take that affects the way your body works. Most drugs were developed for medical purposes. They are dangerous when misused.

Doping means taking drugs to improve sporting performance. It is a big problem in sports. Athletes take drugs for different reasons:

- to pep up their performance
- to kill pain so that they can keep going
- to build muscles faster than they can do by training
- to calm themselves before important events.

An athlete who dopes is cheating. The International Olympic Committee has drawn up a list of banned drugs. It includes the classes of drugs described below. International athletes can be tested for these drugs at any time, and face a ban of at least a year if the test is positive.

Stimulants

These stimulate the circulatory and nervous systems. They raise the heart rate and blood pressure, and speed up reactions. The person feels alert and confident, and can work hard for long periods without feeling pain or fatigue. Examples are:

- **amphetamines**, for example Dexedrine, Benzedrine, 'speed'.
- **caffeine**. This is a natural stimulant found in tea and coffee.

Stimulants are used in medicine to help patients with heart and lung problems. They are misused by athletes who want to improve their performance.

Dangers
- Pain and fatigue are the body's warning signals. If they are suppressed, the athlete carries on too long and risks cramps, strains, and overheating. Overheating can lead to heat stroke.
- When the stimulant has worn off the athlete feels really 'down'.
- Stimulants can cause violent and aggressive behaviour.
- Heavy use causes high blood pressure and liver and brain damage.

A dangerous drug? A caffeine level twenty times above 'normal' would get you banned from the Olympics.

Narcotic analgesics

These are pain-killers. **Narcotic** means causing drowsiness. **Analgesic** means killing pain.

Narcotic analgesics act on the central nervous system and stop the body feeling pain. They give a feeling of well-being, relaxation and sleepiness. They include:

- **morphine** and **heroin**. These are used in hospitals to treat people in severe pain, for example cancer patients.
- **codeine**. This is a much milder drug. There is codeine in many of the pain killers and diaorrhea treatments on sale in chemist shops.

DOPING CONTROL IN SPORT

SPORTS COUNCIL

INTERNATIONAL OLYMPIC COMMITTEE
DOPING CLASSES AND METHODS: EXAMPLES

STIMULANTS e.g. amphetamine, cocaine, ephedrine and related compounds

NARCOTIC ANALGESICS e.g. codeine, morphine, pethidine and related compounds

ANABOLIC STEROIDS e.g. nandrolone, stanozolol, testosterone and related compounds

BETA BLOCKERS e.g. acebutolol, atenolol, propranolol and related compounds

DIURETICS e.g. frusimide, hydrochlorothiazide, spironolactone, triamaterine and related compounds

PEPTIDE HORMONES & ANALOGUES e.g. growth hormone, HCG, ACTH

BLOOD DOPING,

PHARMACOLOGICAL, CHEMICAL AND PHYSICAL MANIPULATION

Classes of drugs subject to certain restrictions

ALCOHOL, MARIJUANA e.g. (not prohibited but may be restricted)

LOCAL ANAESTHETICS, CORTICOSTEROIDS (except for approved treatments)

TREATMENT GUIDELINES:
EXAMPLES OF PERMITTED AND PROHIBITED SUBSTANCES
(based upon International Olympic Committee Doping Classes)

ASTHMA: ALLOWED – Terbutlaine, Salbutamol, Ventolin, Intal, Becotide. N.B Inhalers Only.

COUGH: ALLOWED – steam and menthol inhalations. Benylin Expectorant. All antibiotics.
BANNED – products containing codeine, ephedrines, phenylpropanolamine

DIARRHOEA: ALLOWED – Dioralyte, Lomotil, Motilium.
BANNED – products containing codeine or morphine

HAYFEVER: ALLOWED – Antihistamines, Triludan, Piriton, Histryll, Beconase, Otrivine, Opticrom eye drops.
BANNED – products containing ephedrine, pseudoephedrine.

HEADACHE: ALLOWED – Paracetamol, Aspirin, Anadin.
BANNED – products containing codeine, dextropropoxyphene.

SORE THROAT: ALLOWED – Soluble paracetamol gargle.

VOMITING: ALLOWED – Dioralyte, Rehidrat, Maxolon.

WARNING: THE ABOVE ARE ONLY EXAMPLES OF SUBSTANCES CURRENTLY PERMITTED OR PROHIBITED.
IF IN DOUBT CHECK WITH YOUR GOVERNING BODY OR THE SPORTS COUNCIL(01 388 1277)
REMEMBER– YOU ARE RESPONSIBLE   JULY 1989

An example of the Intenational Olympic Committee's guidelines on drugs. The list of banned drugs is continually updated.

Some athletes use narcotic analgesics to kill the pain from injury, so that they can carry on competing in events.

Dangers

- Narcotic analgesics cause constipation and low blood pressure.
- They cause extreme apathy.
- They are addictive. (Even codeine has its addicts.) The withdrawal symptoms can be very unpleasant.
- Carrying on in spite of injury will make the injury worse.
- Morphine and heroin are illegal in most countries except for medical use. In some, the punishment for being caught is death.

Anabolic steroids

Anabolic steroids are hormones which help to build and repair muscle and bone. They occur naturally in the body. The male sex hormone **testosterone** is one example. They are also made artificially and used to treat people with wasting diseases.

Some athletes and body builders take artificial steroids to increase the size and strength of their muscles and help them recover from training.

Dangers

If you take artificial anabolic steroids you stop the body making its own. This causes many problems, including:

- heart disease and high blood pressure
- weakened ligaments and tendons
- infertility and cancer
- aggressive behaviour
- the growth of face and body hair, and deepening of the voice, in females.

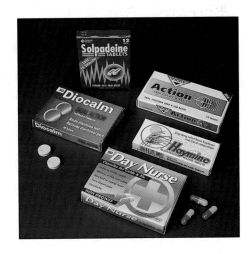

Some over-the-counter medicines contain drugs on the IOC banned list. Athletes must be very careful. The wrong choice in the chemists could mean the end of a career.

Questions

1. What is a *drug*?
2. What does *doping* mean?
3. Athletes who dope are cheats. Explain why.
4. What do stimulants do?
5. Describe three dangers in using stimulants.
6. Explain why an athlete might want to use a narcotic analgesic.
7. What are *anabolic steroids*? Give an example.
8. a Why do athletes use anabolic steroids?
   b Write down four dangers in using them.

9.5 Drugs and sport (II)

Diuretics

These increase the amount of water excreted in urine. They are used to treat patients with heart disease who have excess fluid in their bodies.

They are misused by boxers and wrestlers who want to lose weight quickly before the weigh-in for a match, so that they qualify for their group. They are also misused by athletes who drink lots of water to flush out traces of other banned drugs.

Dangers
- Sodium and potassium salts get eliminated as well as water. The body needs these salts.
- Low levels of potassium lead to muscle weakness and heart damage.

Drugs to reduce anxiety

Beta blockers. When you are anxious, the hormone adrenaline is released into your blood. It makes your heart beat faster and your palms sweat. It speeds up your breathing, and the conversion of glycogen to glucose in your muscles. You are ready for *fight or flight*.

Beta blockers block the effect of adrenaline. They slow down the heart and breathing. They are used in hospitals to treat patients with high blood pressure and heart disease. They are misused by athletes to calm their nerves before important events.

Beta blockers are banned in archery and shooting as well as some other sports. Can you explain why?

Dangers
- They can reduce blood pressure so much that the user faints.
- They lower performance during lengthy (endurance) events.
- They can cause sleeplessness, nightmares and depression.

Tranquillisers. These reduce anxiety and calm you down. Examples are Librium and Valium.

Dangers
- They make the person feel dull and lacking in energy.
- They are addictive and can be very hard to give up.

Blood doping

Oxygen is carried in red blood cells. The more red cells you have, the more oxygen reaches the muscles. This helps them work for longer.

In **blood doping**, an athlete withdraws blood a few weeks before an important event. The red cells are separated and frozen. Just before the event they are thawed and injected back into the athlete.

Dangers
- All blood transfusions and injections carry a risk of infection.
- Top athletes already have a high concentration of red cells. Adding more may block their capillaries.

All medal winners at the Olympics and the Commonwealth games are routinely tested for drugs. If the test is positive it means disgrace, as it did for this British athlete.

Socially acceptable drugs

Nicotine and alcohol are socially acceptable drugs. But that does not mean they are good for you! Both of them lower your fitness.

Smoking

This is what you get in a cigarette:

- **nicotine** which is a poison. It is addictive. It makes your heart rate and blood pressure rise. It makes new smokers dizzy. It causes heart disease.
- **tar**, which is treacly brown stuff that collects in your lungs and respiratory system. It contains thousands of different chemicals. It clogs the lungs and stops you breathing properly. It causes lung cancer and bronchitis.
- **carbon monoxide**, which is a poisonous gas in the smoke. In your lungs, red blood cells pick it up in place of oxygen. Less oxygen reaches your muscles and the rest of your body.

There is no 'safe' level of smoking. Every cigarette is dangerous. In the UK around 111 000 people a year die from diseases caused by smoking and around 2000 have legs amputated.

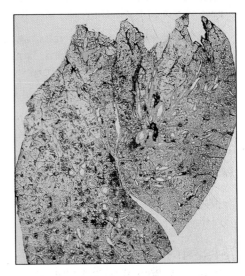

A section through a smoker's lung showing tar deposits. Imagine trying to breathe through that lot!

Alcohol

All alcoholic drinks contain a chemical called **ethanol**. It is what makes people drunk. It doesn't do much harm in *small* quantities. But larger quantities are dangerous.

- Alcohol affects co-ordination, judgement, balance, speech and hearing.
- It can make people aggressive.
- It causes the blood vessels of the skin to dilate, so you rapidly lose body heat. This can be fatal outside in cold weather.
- It lowers the level of glycogen in your muscles. This means they can't work so long or so hard.
- Athletes who drink too much lose their drive to train and compete.
- Long-term alcohol abuse leads to kidney and liver damage.

After heavy drinking, there will still be alcohol in the blood next day. Alcohol the day before an important event is a very bad idea.

Questions

1. What does a *diuretic* do?
2. Why might boxers want to use diuretics?
3. a Explain how beta blockers work.
   b Name one side-effect.
4. In theory, blood doping should improve an athlete's performance. Explain why.
5. Name the substance in cigarettes that causes heart rate to increase.
6. Why does smoking reduce the amount of oxygen that reaches muscles? Give two reasons.
7. It is not possible to be a heavy drinker *and* a top athlete. Explain why.

9.6 Hygiene and foot care

Sweating

You have about three million sweat glands in your skin. During hard exercise in hot weather you can lose up to 3 litres of sweat *an hour*.

Sweat is water containing salts, ammonia and other wastes.
It does not smell to start with. But the bacteria that live on your skin feed on it and produce smelly substances.

It is important to shower and change your underclothes often to get rid of these smelly substances, and especially after exercise.

Deodorants and **antiperspirants** help you avoid sweaty smells. Deodorants mask the smell of sweat with a nicer smell. Antiperspirants coat the sweat pores with a film so the sweat can't get out. Since sweat helps you during sport, using an antiperspirant before a game is not a good idea.

Choice of clothing

Sports clothing must let you move freely. It must also let you sweat freely since sweat is your body's normal way to cool. Light loose cotton or cotton-polyester clothing is good for hot weather. Shorts and short-sleeved tops expose plenty of skin for sweat to evaporate.

In cold weather it is a good idea to wear several layers. The layers trap heat between them. You can then peel off layers as you get warmer. Cover your head and hands if it's very cold.

Remember, you sweat during exercise even in cold weather. Sports clothing should be washed frequently to remove sweat and bacteria.

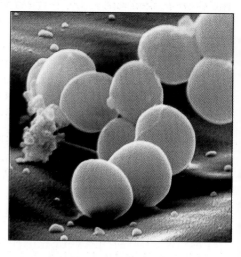

Some of the bacteria that live on your skin and feed on sweat (magnified by 30 000). These are usually harmless. But if they multiply inside blocked pores you'll get a boil or pimple.

Clothes like these are fine for summer sports – but white clothes are even cooler!

Foot infections

Athlete's foot This is a fungus that grows between your toes, making the skin cracked and itchy. It spreads from one person to another by direct contact, or you can pick it up from socks, towels and wet changing room floors.

To avoid athlete's foot, take care where you walk in your bare feet. Use flip-flops around swimming pools. Wash your feet often and dry them carefully between the toes. Avoid socks and shoes that make your feet sweaty. A fungus likes warm damp places!

Veruccas These are flat warts that grow on the soles of your feet. They usually grow where your weight falls, so they can be painful. They are caused by a virus and they spread in the same way as athlete's foot.

Veruccas are very contagious. If you have them, wear flip-flops in the changing room to stop them spreading!

To treat athletes foot you'll find sprays, powder and ointment in the chemist's. For verrucas you'll find ointments and medicated pads.

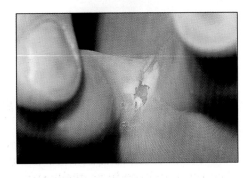

Watch out, there's athlete's foot about. It is highly contagious.

Corns, bunions and blisters

Shoes that are too tight can cause corns, bunions and blisters.

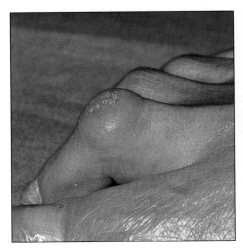

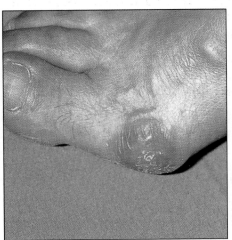

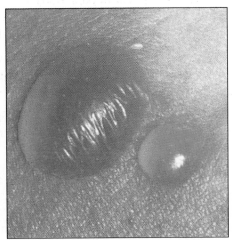

Corns are pads of thick hard skin that form on the toes and soles of feet. They can be very painful. Corn plasters may help, or go to a chiropodist.

At the joint of your big toe is a cushion of liquid called a **bursa**. If it gets inflamed the result is a **bunion**. If a bunion is very painful you will need surgery.

Friction causes skin to **blister**. Don't burst a blister. If it does burst keep it clean and dry and cover it with gauze. Don't pick off the scab that forms.

Questions

1 What makes sweat smell?
2 What does a deodorant do?
3 What does an antiperspirant do?
4 Why are shorts better than jogging bottoms for tennis on a hot day?
5 How would you know if you had athlete's foot?

6 Write down three things you can do to avoid catching athlete's foot.
7 What is a *verucca*? How would you treat it?
8 What is: **a** a corn? **b** a bunion?
9 Name three problems caused by wearing shoes that are too tight for you.

Questions on Chapter 9

1 Which statement is *not* true?
   A Vitamin C is needed for healthy gums.
   B A gram of fat gives over twice as much energy as a gram of protein.
   C Vitamins give you energy.
   D Calcium, iodine and iron are minerals.

2 Match each substance i - v below to one of the statements A to E.
   A helps move food through your gut faster
   B your blood could not carry oxygen without it
   C the body's first choice for energy
   D is found in every cell in your body
   E needed for the hormones that control how fast you burn up food

   i   water
   ii   carbohydrates
   iii iodine
   iv   fibre
   v   iron

3 Name four foods you could eat to obtain this substance:
   a carbohydrate
   b vitamin C
   c protein
   d fibre
   e fat
   f vitamin A

4 a What is *basal metabolic rate*?
   b You need energy even when you are lying down perfectly still. Explain why.
   c The bigger you are, the bigger your basal metabolic rate is. See if you can explain why.

5 Arrange these in order of how much they need to eat. The person who needs to eat least should come first:

   a male student of 17
   a retired woman of 75
   a coal miner of 40
   a boy of 12
   a female student of 17

6 a What is a *healthy balanced diet*?
   b What proportion of carbohydrates, fats and proteins should you eat for a healthy balanced diet?
   c Write down six guidelines for a healthy balanced diet.
   d Grilling is a healthier way than frying, to cook fish and meat. Explain why.
   e Give three examples of processed foods.
   f What are *food additives*?
   g A diet of only processed foods is unhealthy. Explain.

7 Say whether the statement is true or false.
   a You should take 55% of your carbohydrate in the form of sugar.
   b If you need more energy than your diet provides, the extra is obtained from stored fat.
   c Potatoes provide you with vitamin C.
   d You need more vitamins and minerals when you are training hard.
   e Lean meat is high in fibre.

8 1 kg of body fat is equivalent to 32 000 kJ of energy. Suppose your energy needs are 10 000 kJ per day, and you eat enough food to provide 14 000 kJ per day.
   a How much more energy do you take in per day than you need?
   b Are you eating too much food for your needs, or too little?
   c What happens to this extra food?
   d At this rate, how long would it take you to gain an extra kilogram in weight?

9 One can of orange barley Lucozade contains:

protein	a trace
fat	almost none
carbohydrate	63.03 g
energy	1089 kJ

   a Which nutrient provides the energy in Lucozade?
   b Suppose you need 10 000 kJ of energy a day. About how many cans of Lucozade would you need to drink to get this energy?
   c A diet that consisted only of Lucozade would be a bad idea. Give at least four reasons.
   d In Lucozade, the carbohydrate is in the form of glucose. You get energy faster from Lucozade than from eating spaghetti. Why do you think this is?

10 A small tin of baked beans contains:

protein	9.6 g
fat	0.4 g
carbohydrate	27.9 g
fibre	7.6 g
salt	2.5 g
energy	640 kJ

   a Baked beans are a good source of fibre. Why is fibre good for you?
   b You should eat around 18g of fibre a day. What could you eat with baked beans to provide more fibre?
   c You should eat no more than 1.6 g of salt a day. Why is too much salt harmful?
   d What advice would you give the makers of baked beans about the amount of salt they use?

11 A unit called the calorie is also used to measure the energy value of food. Labels will show both kilocalories and kilojoules. Copy and complete:

a 1 kilocalorie = _____ calories

b 1 kilocalorie = _____ kilojoules

c 50 kilocalories = _____ kilojoules

12 Copy and complete the paragraph correctly, by writing *carbohydrates* or *fats* in each space.

Your body uses both _____ and _____ for energy. _____ give more energy per gram. _____ are easier to digest. For intense exercise you use mainly _____, in the form of glycogen. For endurance events such as marathon running, you depend more on _____. The fitter you are, the more readily you can burn up _____.

13 Muscles can use both carbohydrate (glycogen) and fat for energy. As this bar graph shows, the extent to which your muscles depend on each source depends on the activity:

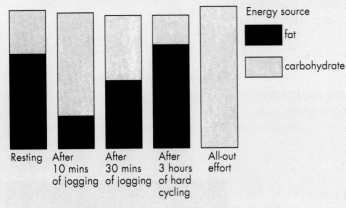

Energy source

■ fat

□ carbohydrate

Resting | After 10 mins of jogging | After 30 mins of jogging | After 3 hours of hard cycling | All-out effort

Which is the main source of energy used in:

a the Tour de France?

b boxing (each round 3 minutes)?

c resting?

d a 20-minute jog?

e the 100m sprint?

14 a Write down all the reasons you can think of why sports people should not use drugs.

b Which reason do *you* think is the most important?

15 Write down two harmful effects of using:

a stimulants

b anabolic steroids

c pain killers during exercise

16 a Which substance in alcohol makes you drunk?

b Write down five ways in which alcohol will affect a competitor's performance, during a sports event.

17 a Cigarettes contain an addictive substance which is poisonous. What is it called?

b Cigarette packets carry the message 'Smoking can kill'. Name five ways in which smoking is harmful.

Things to do

A calculator will help for some of these.

1 Before you do activities 2 - 5 you will need to:

a collect labels from at least one chocolate bar and one packet of crisps, showing how much energy they give.

b weigh yourself in kilograms.

2 This table shows the amount of energy burned up per kilogram of body weight per minute, for different levels of activity.

Energy used in ...	kJ per kilogram per minute
resting	0.13
moderate exercise (eg jogging or swimming)	0.59
vigorous exercise (eg football or netball)	0.79

a Calculate much energy you burn up per minute when you are resting. (0.13 kJ × your weight)

b Calculate how much you burn up per minute during moderate exercise. (0.59 kJ × your weight)

c Calculate how much you burn up per minute during vigorous exercise. (0.79 kJ × your weight)

3 A Picnic bar provides 960 kJ of energy. If you weigh 60 kg, you burn up 7.8 kJ of energy per minute when resting. So it will take you (960 ÷ 7.8) minutes to burn up the energy from the Picnic bar. That is 123 minutes, or 2 hours 3 minutes.

a Look at your chocolate bar label. How much energy does the bar provide?

b Work out how many minutes it would take you to use up this energy during vigorous exercise.

c Look at the crisps packet label. How much energy do the crisps provide?

d Work out how long it would take to work off this energy during moderate exercise.

4 1 g of body fat is equivalent to 3.2 kJ of energy.

If you do not burn off your chocolate bar, work out how much weight you will gain from it.

5 Repeat exercise 4 for the packet of crisps.

6 Keep a record of everything you eat for one week.

a Try to work out what proportion of carbohydrates, fats and proteins you ate. (Labels on food packets will help you.)

b Try to estimate how much energy this food has provided. Then work out your average daily energy intake.

c Assume your energy needs are 11 000 kJ if you are male and 9000 kJ if you are female. Did you eat too much? Or too little?

d Did you eat a healthy balanced diet? Explain.

10.1 Skill in sport

How do you succeed at a sport? The main ingredient you need is **skill**. That's something you can learn!

What is skill?

Skill is the learned ability to bring about a pre-determined result with maximum certainty and efficiency.

In other words, skill means you can perform an activity or movement to get exactly the result you intended, without wasting energy or time.

Think about these phrases:

- **learned ability**. Skill is something you learn. You are not born with it. You improve with practice.
- **pre-determined result**. This means you have an aim you set out to achieve. For example breaking a serve in tennis.
- **maximum certainty**. You are very likely to be successful. A skilful athlete can perform a movement successfully time after time. Getting it right once by chance is not skill.
- **maximum efficiency**. You perfom the movement smoothly, without wasting any energy or time.

Skill at tennis means you have full control of your body, the racket and the ball. You place your shots exactly where you want, at the speed you want. You are **skilful**.

Other meanings of skill

The word **skill** is also used in two other ways in sport. It means:

- the sport itself, for example cricket or tennis.
- a particular movement or action, for example a forward roll in gymnastics. Here it is short for **motor skill**. (*Motor* means movement.)

Sports are made up of motor skills. Think about the different motor skills that make up tennis: serve, backhand, drop shot and so on.

Some motor skills are common to many sports. Running and jumping are examples. Some are specific to one sport. The front crawl is specific to swimming.

Basic and complex skills

Running, jumping and floating on your back in the water are examples of simple or **basic** skills.

Other motor skills are **complex**. For example the tennis serve, the high jump and the back stroke in swimming. Can you think of a complex skill in gymnastics?

You need to master basic skills before you move on to complex ones. Complex skills can be difficult to learn, and need a lot of practice.

The complex skills required in fencing can take a long time to master.

Open and closed skills

An **open skill** is one where your movements vary, depending on what is going on around you. It depends on your **environment**. For example on where your opponent is (netball) or on the wind direction (sailing). A **closed skill** is one where the movements are always exactly the same. They do not depend on the environment.

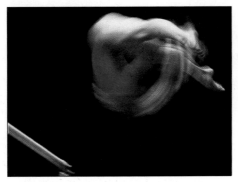

A goalkeeper saving a goal. This is an **open** skill. His move depends on where the ball is coming from. So next time it will be different.

A gymnast practising a somersault. This is a **closed** skill. She will repeat it exactly next time. Her environment is stable and does not affect her.

Look at this tennis serve. Next time the player will repeat the moves but change the timing and placing of the shot. So is the skill closed or open?

For the tennis serve, the sequence of movements is closed. But the timing and placing of the shot depend on the position of the player and his opponent. In that respect the serve is open. You can place it between closed and open on a continuous scale or **continuum**.

closed   open

forward roll   tennis serve   rugby hook   saving a goal

Most motor skills, and sports, lie somewhere between closed and open. Hooking the ball in a rugby scrum is another example.

Skill and performance

Each attempt you make at a skill is a **performance**. The more skilful you are, the better your performance is likely to be. But it does not depend *only* on skill. It is also affected by other factors. If you are feeling nervous or tired, or the weather is too hot, your performance may suffer.

Because open skills depend on what is going on around you, they are affected by more factors than closed skills are. For example they are affected by the actions of your team mates and your opponents.

Factors affecting an athlete's performance in a sports event:

- body type – does it suit that sport?
- level of skill
- general fitness
- skills-related fitness, specific to the sport
- preparation in terms of diet
- mental preparation – does he or she have a goal in mind? is he or she motivated?
- psychological state – too nervous about the event? or too laid back?
- physical condition on the day – tired? ill? injured?
- drugs, including alcohol and smoking
- the environment – for example too hot? too cold? too windy?
- the actions of team-mates and opponents

Questions

1 Steve Hendry is *skilful* at snooker. Explain what that means.
2 Explain how the environment changes for:
  a a rugby player   b a golfer   c a windsurfer
3 Place these on an open-closed continuum:
  a a penalty kick   b the breast stroke   c jogging
  d dribbling a ball through the defence
4 A skilful athlete *always* perfoms well. True or false?

10.2 Information processing

Whether you're playing tennis or throwing the discus or washing the dishes, your brain is in control. It processes information from your eyes, ears, skin and muscles, then tells your muscles what to do.

The information processing system

This diagram shows the stages in processing information.

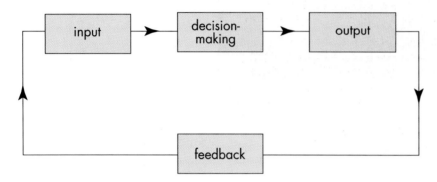

The information processing system

Input

Input means the information you receive. In sport you take information in through your **eyes** and **ears**. For example in tennis you see your opponent hitting the ball and hear the thwack.

But that's not all. You also **feel** a lot of information within your body. You feel how hard your hand is grasping the racket, and the position of your limbs, and how ready your muscles are to respond.

This awareness of your own body is called **proprioception**. It is made up of information from your skin, your muscles, and the tiny organs inside your ears whose job is to detect balance.

Decision-making

Next your brain must decide how to respond to the input. The decision will have a big effect on the quality of your performance. Decision-making involves **perception** and **memory**.

Perception. This is the process of **interpreting** information. Suppose your opponent lobs the ball towards you. From what you hear and see and feel, your brain will judge:

- how hard the ball was struck
- how fast it is moving
- where and when it will arrive
- where your opponent will be standing by then
- how prepared you are.

Then it decides how you should respond. But it can't do any of this without memory.

If you've never seen a shuttlecock before, you won't know how hard to hit it. There's nothing stored in your memory to help your brain make decisions.

Memory. Your memory has two parts: short-term and long-term.

Short-term memory is your 'work space'. All the information you receive goes in there. It stays only a short time - about two minutes at most. If you ignore it, it fades very quickly. Paying attention holds it for longer. By concentrating you can transfer it to your long-term memory.

Long-term memory is your 'library'. It holds images, tastes, sounds, smells, feelings and actions you are familiar with, and all the sports skills you have learned and practised. It can hold a limitless amount of information, and store it for a lifetime.

How perception depends on memory. A great deal of information arrives in your short-term memory at any one time. Your brain ignores most of it, and focuses on what seems important. (This is called **selective attention**.) It interprets this information by scanning your long-term memory for similar information from before. Then it decides on suitable action.

If you have learned your tennis well and practised a lot, your long-term memory will have everything you need for interpreting the information you receive during a tennis match, plus programmes of instructions for action.

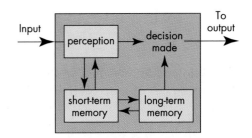

Decision-making

Output

This is the action you take as a result of your brain's decision. For example you might play a drop shot.

If your information processing is working well, and your long-term memory is well stocked with skills, your output is likely to be successful.

Feedback

Feedback is the response you receive to your output. It tells you whether the output was successful or not. For example:

- you can usually *feel* whether a shot was good or bad
- the score changes
- your opponent misses the shot
- if it's a practice match, your coach may say something to you.

Note that an arrow goes from **feedback** to **input**, completing the loop. Feedback becomes part of input. It will affect your next decision. Feedback from your coach helps you learn and improve. You will find out more about this in Unit 10.4.

A figure skater waits nervously for her marks – feedback – from the judges to see if she's a medal winner.

Questions

1 Draw a simple diagram to show how you process information when playing your sport.
2 What is *proprioception*? Give two examples from your own sport.
3 What is *perception*? How is it linked to memory?
4 Describe the two kinds of memory you've got.
5 If you are just starting tennis, you probably won't play very well. Why?
6 What is: a output? b feedback? Give two examples of each from your sport.

10.3 Learning a new skill

How do you know when you've learned a new skill? When your performances of it are **consistently correct**.

How to learn a new skill

You use your information processing system to **learn** a skill as well as perform it. So what's the best way to learn? These ideas will help you.

- Your information processing system can process only a limited amount of information at a time. It has **limited channel capacity**.
- If you try to process too much information at a time, the system gets **overloaded**. You feel confused.

> . . . . then shift **all** your weight to your left foot, bend your left knee, swing your right leg through a hundred and eighty degrees, flex your left elbow, take a deep breath and . . . .

> HELP!

- This means you learn best when there are no distractions. Noise and chatter use up some of your limited channel capacity.
- It also means you shouldn't try to learn too much at once. If you do you'll suffer from overload. If you tried to learn the tennis serve all at once you probably wouldn't succeed. The best way is to break it into parts and learn each separately.
- To help avoid overload, instructions from your coach should be clear, simple and to the point.
- The instructions should concentrate on the most important aspects of the skill at first. Your brain will focus on these through selective attention.
- When your coach demonstrates a new skill, it goes into your short-term memory. Learning it means moving it into your long-term memory. You do this by **practice**.
- Your long-term memory can hold an almost limitless amount of information, and it is permanent. Once you have learned to swim or ride a bike you do not forget, although you may feel 'rusty'.

Types of practice

You have to practise a new skill many times before you've really learned it. The best way to practise depends on the skill.

- If it's a basic skill such as catching a netball, you can practise the whole skill. This is called **whole practice**. Then you can move on to practise it within a netball game.

The lay-up shot in basketball is a complex skill that lends itself to part practice.

- If it's a complex skill, you should watch someone perform it first, and perhaps even try it out, to get a feeling for it. Then break it down and practise it in parts. This is called **part practice**.
  For example with a tennis serve you could practise the toss, then the swing and so on. Then put the parts together and practise the whole skill. And finally, try it in a game of tennis.
- When you're practising an open skill, for example dribbling a basketball, you should practise it in lots of different situations. This is called **variable practice**.
  It is important because your movements in an open skill will vary, depending on the environment.
- When you're practising a closed skill, keep repeating it under the same conditions. This is called **fixed practice**.
- When you are practising a skill within a game, it is usually best to work in small groups to begin with. This way you won't have to pay attention to too many other players, which might confuse you.

Types of guidance

When you are learning and practising a skill, you usually need help or **guidance** from a teacher, coach or friend. This becomes **input** for your information processing system.

There are three types of guidance: **visual**, **verbal** and **manual**. A good coach will use more than one kind.

Visual guidance. This is guidance you can *look at*: demonstrations, video, posters and wall charts. Visual guidance is especially useful when you are just starting to learn a new skill.

Verbal guidance. This is guidance you can *listen to*. The coach explains in words what you should do. It is useful because he or she can explain on the spot, repeat the instructions as often as needed, and tailor them to suit you.

Manual guidance. This is guidance you can *feel*, where:

- the coach takes hold of you and guides you through the movement, for example a difficult dance routine
- or a device is used to restrict your movement and keep you safe, for example a swimming float or a climbing tight rope.

Manual guidance is useful where a skill is very complex, or dangerous, or you are scared. It gets you used to the movements for the skill before you try them out on your own.

A mixture of verbal and manual guidance.

Questions

1 Your information processing system has *limited channel capacity*. What does that mean?
2 Why should you not try to learn too much at once?
3 When a coach is giving you instructions, he or she should stick to the point and not ramble. Why?
4 How does a skill get transferred into your long-term memory?

5 What is *part practice*? When is it useful?
6 After part practice, it is important to put the parts together and do whole practice. Why?
7 Why is variable practice important for open skills?
8 Name and describe the three types of guidance.
9 For each type of guidance, try to think of:
  a two advantages b two disadvantages

10.4 Feedback and learning

If you want to learn fast and well, pay attention to feedback!

What is feedback?

As you saw on page 117, **feedback** is the response you get to your
performance or **output** in the information processing system.
For example your score might rise, or your opponent might miss
the shot, or your coach might say 'Well done'.
Feedback in turn becomes part of input, as the arrow shows:

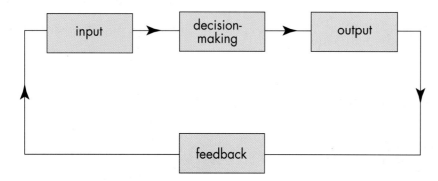

The information processing system

Two kinds of feedback

Feedback in sport can be divided into two kinds: **knowledge of
performance** and **knowledge of results**.

Knowledge of performance (KP) tells you how well, or badly, you
performed. For example how smooth your serve was, or your
somersault.

- Some KP comes from **proprioception** - your own body awareness.
  You can feel how hard you hit a shot or kick a ball.
- Your coach and friends will provide KP.
- Recording your performance on video, and watching it later with
  your coach, is a good way to obtain KP.

Note that feedback from proprioception is called **internal** feedback.
Why? Feedback from outside you is **external** feedback.

Knowledge of results (KR) tells you the outcome of your actions.

- You obtain KR when you watch the football fly into the net, or see
  how far you've thrown the javelin.
- The announcement of the score, or a cheer from your supporters,
  also provides KR.
- You can sometimes get KR from proprioception. At the end of a
  somersault on the trampoline, you can tell if you've landed correctly.

Both KP and KR will help you improve your performance.
For example KR tells you that you've landed badly from a somersault.
But you don't know the reason. Your coach can give you KP and
suggest what to do next time.

120

If you're a racing driver like Damon Hill, technical data will provide knowledge of performance.

Terry Venables providing knowledge of performance during an England squad training session.

The importance of feedback

When you are learning a new skill, feedback from others is very important.

* Encouraging feedback will motivate you to try harder.
* When you are told your performance was good, it helps to reinforce the skill in your mind.
* Feedback on ways to improve your performance helps you become more and more skilful.

The principles of feedback

There are four principles of feedback.

1 There can be no learning without feedback. And KR alone is not enough. You won't improve much without KP.
2 Feedback should be given as soon as possible after the attempt. The longer the delay, the less useful feedback will be in correcting errors.
3 It should be clear, correct and to the point. If you don't understand it, you won't know what to change at the next attempt.
4 You must have enough time to process the feedback before the next attempt. If you get too much feedback too quickly, without time to process it, you will just get confused.

Feedback from others is especially important when you are a beginner. But when you get more experience, you can often detect your own errors and you may even know how to correct them.

Questions

1 What is *feedback*? Give three examples.
2 Name the two kinds of feedback in sport.
3 a Give three examples of ways to obtain KP.
  b Which of these do you think is best? Why?
4 KR alone will not help you improve much. Explain why.

5 Imagine you are learning a new and difficult skill. Give three reasons why feedback will help you.
6 Feedback should be given as soon as possible after a performance. Why is this?
7 You must have time to process feedback in your mind before your next attempt. Why?

Questions on Chapter 10

1. Skill is the *learned ability* to bring about a *pre-determined result* with *maximum certainty* and *maximum efficiency*. Explain each of the terms in italics and give an example.

2. Some motor skills are specific to particular sports, and others are more general.
   a. What does the term *motor* mean here?
   b. Name a motor skill which is common to:
      i. both basketball and netball
      ii. both badminton and tennis
   c. Name a motor skill which is specific to:
      i. golf   ii. swimming

3. Many sports fall between closed and open on a continuum, like this:

closed   open
archery   potholing

   a. What is a *continuum*?
   b. Draw a continuum and mark these sports on it:
      swimming rugby badminton gymnastics canoeing
   c. Draw a continuum and mark these skills on it:
      a free throw in basketball   the front crawl
      tacking (windsurfing)   putting (golf)

4. a. Draw a diagram of the information processing system, and label the parts.
   b. In processing information, what is meant by:
      i. input?   ii. decision making?   iii. output?
      iv. feedback?   v. overload?   vi. selective attention?
      Give one example of each.

5.

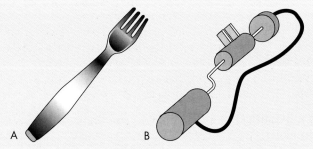

A   B

   a. What object is represented by drawing A above? Write down your answer.
   b. You used your information system to answer **a**.
      i. How did you take in the input?
      ii. How did you identify the image? Describe the process using these terms: perception, short-term memory, long-term memory decision-making.
   c. What was your *output* in **a**?
   d. How might you obtain feedback?
   e. Now what does drawing B represent?
   f. If you cannot identify B, explain why.

6. a. What is *proprioception*?
   b. Give four examples of information a cyclist would obtain through proprioception.

7. a. How can you tell when you have learned a skill?
   b. To learn a skill you must transfer it to your long-term memory. How do you do this?
   c. Explain why it is better to break some skills down into parts to learn them.
   d. Give one example of a skill from your sport which could be learned in parts.
   e. Which of these skills would *not* be suitable to learn in parts? See if you can explain why.
      i. running   ii. the backhand in tennis
      iii. the breast stroke   iv. bouncing a ball
      v. a somersault   vi. throwing a javelin
   f. Think of one disadvantage of learning a skill in parts. How would you overcome this disadvantage?

8. You are going to teach the front crawl to a friend who can already swim.
   a. Would you break the skill down into parts? Why?
   b. Would you demonstrate the whole skill first? Why?
   c. Do you think it would help to let your friend try the whole skill early on? Why?
   d. Make a plan showing how you would teach the stroke to your friend, and what kind of practice you'd ask him or her to do.

9. a. Name three different forms of guidance and give an example of each. (Find an example you have not used before.)
   b. When teaching the front crawl to your friend in question 8, which kind(s) of guidance would you use?
   c. Explain why your task is likely to be more difficult and less successful if you rely on:
      i. visual guidance only   ii. verbal guidance only
      iii. manual guidance only

10. There are two kinds of feedback: knowledge of performance (KP) and knowledge of results (KR). Decide whether the statement represents KP or KR.
    a. You won!
    b. You should have put all your weight on your left leg. Try that next time.
    c. You jumped 3 m 60 cm.
    d. You need to swing your arm back further.

11. You are practising the lay-up in basketball, where you dribble in and jump to shoot the ball off the backboard and into the basket.
    a. How would you obtain KR?
    b. How would you obtain KP?
    c. Why do you need KP as well as KR?

Things to do

1 Investigating proprioception

Stand with your arms stretched out straight and level in front of you. Close your eyes. Swing one arm up and the other down. Now return them to their original position.

When you think they're back where they started, open your eyes and check.

With your eyes closed, you depend on proprioception to know the position of your arms. If they were level when you checked, it shows good proprioception.

2 Investigating selective attention

Selective attention means that your brain attends to only some of the input it receives, and ignores the rest.

Experiments A and B will help you investigate it. For B you will need a flash card with seven numbers written on it. The numbers should all be between 0 and 10, in random order.

Experiment A

a Stand in front of the class. Speaking slowly and clearly, call out 7 letters of the alphabet in random order. (Make a note of the letters you have used.)

b When you have finished, the class writes them down.

c Write the letters on the board. Everyone checks how many they got right. Write the results in a table like this:

Number of letters correct	0	1	2	3	4	5	6	7
Number of students								

Experiment B

a This time hold up the flash card and tell the students to concentrate on the numbers, while you call out 7 more letters of the alphabet, as before, in random order. (Again, keep a note of them.)

b Now ask the class to write down the seven letters.

c Write the correct letters on the board. Ask the class to count how many they got right.

d Write the results in a table like this.

Number of letters correct	0	1	2	3	4	5	6	7
Number of students								

e Compare the two tables. What do you find?

f Explain the difference between the tables using the idea of selective attention.

3 Investigating limited channel capacity

You will need two tennis rackets and two tennis balls.

a Count how many times you can bounce a ball on a racket without dropping it.

b Now use the racket to bounce the ball on the ground. Count how many times you can do it without missing.

c Try **a** and **b** together, with one racket in each hand. Count how many times you can do both together.

d In which step did your brain have most information to deal with: **a**, **b** or **c**?

e Explain your results using the idea of limited channel capacity.

4 Investigating memory

i Place around 15 everyday objects randomly on the table or a tray. Allow the class to look at them for 15 seconds.

ii Now cover the objects or remove the tray. Each person writes a list of the objects.

iii The class looks again at the objects, for one minute. Each person writes another list.

iv Each person switches lists with a partner, and counts the number of correct objects on the partner's list.

a Compare the results for the first list. About how many objects did most people manage to list correctly? (Try designing a bar chart to show the results.)

b What does that tell you about short-term memory?

c How did the score change on the second attempt? Why do you think this was?

d Do you think anyone will remember the objects tomorrow? Check it out!

e How do you think the results would change if you placed related objects together? (For example pencil, pen and ruler together.) Why? Design an experiment to test this.

5 Investigating feedback

The class should divide into three groups. Each group has the same task: to draw ten 5-cm lines while blindfolded.

i Group A will receive no feedback, group B will receive knowledge of results (KR) only, and group C will receive knowledge of performance (KP).

ii Those in group A can work alone. Those in B and C will work in pairs. One person in each pair measures the lines and provides the feedback.

iii When you measure a line write the measurement beside it, to help you compare the results.

a Group A: put on the blindfold and draw the ten lines. Now measure them to see how you did.

b Group B: after each attempt, the person providing feedback measures the line and calls out 'Yes' or 'No'. He or she says nothing more.

c Group C: after each attempt, the person providing feedback describes how close the attempt was to success, and gives a little encouragement. For example 'Good. Just half a centimetre too short.'

Compare the results for the three groups. Which group gave the best performance? What does that teach you about feedback?

11.1 Motivation and goal setting

What makes you put effort into your sport? How can you stay motivated? This Unit will give you some ideas.

Motivation

Motivation is the driving force that makes you do what you do, and determines how much effort you put in. The more motivated you are about something the harder you will work at it, and the more likely you are to succeed.

Your motivation may be **intrinsic** or **extrinsic** or a mixture of the two.

Intrinsic motivation means you do something because you get satisfaction from it. The drive comes from the activity itself. (*Intrinsic* means built in.) If you play a sport because you enjoy it and feel proud of your skill at it, you are intrinsically motivated.

Extrinsic motivation means you do something in order to earn money from it, or win a prize, or please another person. It is called *extrinsic* because it comes from outside.

Extrinsic motivators such as trophies and medals are used a great deal to encourage athletes. The Davis Cup for golf and the FA Cup for football are examples. Money is an important motivator in some sports. The winner of the men's singles at Wimbledon gets a cheque for around £400 000! There are many award schemes to attract young people to sport, set up by companies and sports bodies.

Extrinsic motivators are useful. But they don't always work.

- Not everyone feels rewards are important. (Do you?)
- If a reward is too difficult to obtain, or too easy, it may put you off.
- Competition for prizes may put you under too much pressure.
- A reward may lower your motivation because you feel someone has 'bought' you.
- Athletes may lose interest in their sport if they fail to get a prize.

But if you are intrinsically motivated, you will stick with your sport regardless of rewards. So coaches must ensure that their athletes enjoy the sport. Then when the rewards stop, the athlete doesn't.

It's only a piece of metal ... but it's a very powerful motivator.

Motivation and goals

One good way to stay motivated is to have a **goal** to work towards. For example your goal could be to perform the forward roll with your legs fully stretched, at your next attempt.

- A goal motivates you to work hard.
- It helps you to prepare mentally for a performance, since you know exactly what you are aiming for.
- It acts like a signpost in your training, giving you direction.
- It also gives you something to check your progress against.
- Having a goal makes you feel less anxious, and more in control.
- Meeting your goal increases your confidence.

What makes a good goal?
Think **SMARTER**!

S is for specific. A goal such as 'I must run faster' is far too vague. 'I must run 30 metres in under 4 seconds at my next attempt' is much more specific. It gives you something definite to aim for.

M is for measurable. '30 metres in under 4 seconds' is a measureable goal. You can easily check whether you've been successful.

A is for agreed. You and your coach should discuss and agree about your goals. If you're not happy with them, they won't motivate you.

R is for realistic. A realistic goal is one you are capable of achieving. '30 metres in under 2 seconds' is unrealistic. If a goal is too difficult it will put you off. But if it's too easy you'll get bored.

T is for time-phased. Your goals should be mapped out in advance to give you direction, and get increasingly difficult. A short-term goal for a tennis beginner could be: 'Serve the ball over the net three times in this training session'. A long-term goal could be: 'Get 80% of my first serves in rather than out, by the end of the season.'

E is for exciting. Exciting and challenging goals help to keep you motivated and stop you getting bored.

R is for recorded. Your goals should be written down. Then you can see clearly where you are going and keep check on your progress. You will feel more confident when you see that your training is well planned and monitored. You will feel better prepared for competitions.

Have a specific goal in mind every time you practice your sport. You'll find it makes a lot of difference.

Questions

1 What is *motivation*?
2 Explain the difference between intrinsic and extrinsic motivation.
3 A young man plays a sport because his friends do. Which type of motivation is this?
4 What motivates *you* to play your sport? (There may be several factors.)
5 Give three examples of extrinsic motivators.
6 Name one extrinsic motivator connected with your sport.
7 Give four reasons why goals help an athlete.
8 List the seven characteristics of a good goal.
9 Map out some sports goals for yourself for the next six months. Discuss them with your teacher.

11.2 Arousal in sport

Arousal is a state of excitement and alertness. Before an exam or a competition you may reach a high level of arousal. These are signs:

- your heartbeat and breathing speed up
- you get sweaty palms
- you may feel nervous and shaky
- your mouth gets dry, and you may even feel sick.

Arousal and performance

Your level of arousal for a sports event will affect your performance. Look at the first graph below:

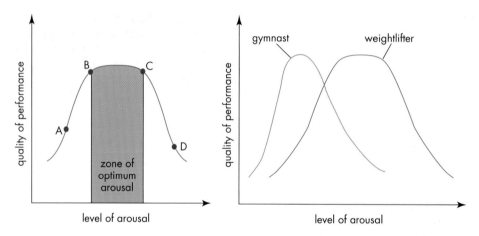

At A, your arousal level is low. Perhaps you are feeling bored or tired. You are not 'psyched up' enough and you perform badly. As arousal increases to B, performance improves. Between B and C your performance is at its best or **optimum**.

But if you are very anxious, your arousal level will rise above C and your performance will suffer. You are over-aroused or 'psyched out'. If it rises to D you will do very badly.

This theory is called the **Inverted U Theory**. Can you see why? BC is called the **zone of optimum arousal**. Why?

Arousal in different sports

Different sports need different levels of arousal. The second graph above shows the curves for a gymnast and a weightlifter. Note that:

- the gymnast performs best at a lower level of arousal. Low arousal is best for sports that depend on fine, precise movements and good timing.
- the weightlifter performs best at a higher level of arousal. High arousal is best for sports that depend on explosive power and large body movements.
- the weightlifter has a broader zone of optimum arousal. This is because increasing arousal has less effect on large powerful movements than on fine, precise ones. It is easier for the gymnast to make mistakes that will spoil her performance.

126

During rehearsals, under-arousal is more likely to be a problem than over-arousal. But it's quite a different matter on opening night.

The USA volleyball coach and his team during the Barcelona Olympics. A coach must know when the team needs psyching up, and when it needs calming down.

Reaching optimum arousal

These are the kind of things that increase arousal:

- a pep talk from your coach before an event
- the warm up before the event
- having a definite goal you intend to achieve in the event
- bright lights and lots of noise around you
- friendly or hostile sports fans looking on.

Coaches know how important it is to reach optimum arousal. Before a competition, a coach may slap a weightlifter's face and give him a whiff of smelling salts. His supporters may shout a lot. But when a gymnast is preparing to compete, the atmosphere is very different. Everyone is calm and quiet. Why?

Controlling anxiety

If you get very anxious before an event, your arousal level may rise above the optimum and spoil your performance. A coach will try to calm and reassure an anxious athlete. There are also things athletes can do to control their anxiety. For example many athletes practice:

- **relaxation**. Techniques include slow deep breathing, and relaxing different muscle groups in turn.
- **visualization**. This is where you go through the event in your mind in advance, in detail. You 'see' yourself performing well and staying calm and confident. It is also called **mental rehearsal**.

Questions

1 What is meant by *arousal*?
2 Give two symptoms of arousal.
3 Explain the Inverted U Theory in your own words.
4 How will boredom affect performance?
5 What is the *zone of optimum arousal*?
6 Give two examples of techniques used in your sport to raise arousal levels.

7 How will anxiety affect performance?
8 Has anxiety ever spoiled your sports performance? Think of steps you could take to reduce it.
9 For each activity, decide whether arousal level should be high or low for optimum performance:
   a beam balance   b shot putt   c sprinting
   d shooting   e rugby   f snooker   g high dive

11.3 Aggression in sport

Aggression in sport can mean two different things:

● acting with intent to injure someone
● acting forcefully within the rules of the sport to achieve your aim.

This Unit deals with just the second meaning.

Are all athletes aggressive?

All athletes show aggressive behaviour. But it's not always obvious!
The more physical contact there is between players, the more obvious
the aggression will be. Look at this diagram:

swimming gymnastics	golf javelin	tennis cricket	netball basketball	boxing rugby
little obvious aggression	aggression against an object	indirect aggression	non-contact aggression	direct aggression

increasing aggression

● **Contact sports** like boxing and rugby rely on physical contact.
  Boxers punch their opponents hard, and rugby players push hard in
  the scrum. This kind of aggression aimed directly at other players is
  called **direct aggression**.
● In sports like netball and basketball there is little physical contact.
  But players can still act aggressively within the rules, for example
  when blocking an opponent in netball.
● In other sports there is no physical contact, but opponents throw
  objects at each other in an attempt to make the other person lose.
  This is called **indirect aggression**. A bowler may hurl a hard fast
  ball straight at the batter in order to intimidate him.
● In some sports the aggression is towards an object. A golfer may hit
  the ball very hard. But he is hitting it towards the next green, and
  not at his opponent.
● In sports like swimming and gymnastics there is no physical contact.
  But even here, an athlete needs an aggressive attitude in order to
  succeed. It takes a huge amount of determination to keep on training
  and competing, especially if you are losing.

Aggressive behaviour can cause injury, even within the rules. In many
sports players must wear protective gear. It is often hard to tell whether
an injury was caused by accident or on purpose. So coaches must
ensure that their players obey the rules. They should not encourage
dirty play, or the attitude that you must win at all costs.

The kit suggests that American football
scores high on aggression.

Questions

1 What does *aggression* in sport mean here?
2 Give two examples of:
  a direct aggression   b indirect aggression

3 How might this person show aggressive behaviour
  within the rules?   a a tennis player   b a shot putter
  c a batsman   d a dancer   e a snooker player

11.4 *Sport and personality*

Your **personality** is the set of characteristics that makes you you.
Are you the shy, quiet type? Or lively and outgoing? Does it affect your
performance in sport? What do you think?

Extrovert or introvert?

There are many ways to classify personality. One way is to classify
people as introverts or extroverts. **Introverts** tend to be calm, shy,
thoughtful, quiet and careful. **Extroverts** are the opposite. They tend
to be lively, sociable, optimistic, outgoing and talkative.

But beware. You can't label someone as extrovert or introvert until you
have observed that person closely, in different situations. For example
in a room full of strangers you may feel quiet and shy even though you
are usually very talkative.

Personality and sport

There has been a lot of research into links between sport and
personality. This table compares the findings about introverts and
extroverts. But remember, these are generalisations, not facts.
A lot more research is needed.

Pot-holing is a solitary activity in many
respects. Suitable for introverts?

Introverts tend to ...	Extroverts tend to ...
• prefer individual sports	• prefer team sports
• prefer a low level of excitement	• prefer a high level of excitement
• work hard in training	• get bored in training
• get nervous before important competitions	• enjoy important competitions
• perform intricate skills well	• get impatient with intricate skills
• enjoy sports with more restricted movements	• enjoy sports with lots of action
• perform better at low levels of arousal	• perform better at high levels of arousal
• dislike contact sports	• enjoy contact sports
• have lower tolerance for pain	• have higher tolerance for pain

Do you think you are introvert or extrovert?
Do the descriptions in the table fit you?

Questions

1 What is an *introvert*?
2 What is an *extrovert*?
3 Why is it a bad idea to label people too quickly?

4 Which type of personality is likely to be attracted to:
a boxing? b gymnastics? c rugby?
d cross country running? e weightlifting

Questions on Chapter 11

1 Below are some reasons for taking part in a sport. Match each item i - iv to a letter A or B.
A extrinsic motivation
B intrinsic motivation

i wanting to please a parent or teacher
ii enjoying the movements in the sport
iii wanting to win the gold medal
iv wanting to improve your skill

2 You probably have several motives for playing your favourite sport.
a Make a list of them.
b Now place them in order of importance.
c Beside each, write down whether it is intrinsic or extrinsic.
d Which are more important to you, the intrinsic or extrinsic motives?

3 a What is a *goal*?
b Here are two different goals:
i to do my best in this event
ii to do 5 more press-ups today than yesterday, within the same time
Which is a better goal? Explain why.

4 A good goal can be summed up by SMARTER.
a What term does each letter stand for?
b Explain what each term means.

5
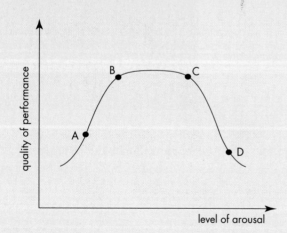

This graph shows the effect of arousal on performance.
a Where on the curve should you be, to give your best performance?
b What is this area of the curve called?
c At A, do you need to calm down or get more psyched up, in order to improve your performance?
d Name one way to bring about this change.
e Name one technique that would help you move from D to C on the curve.

6
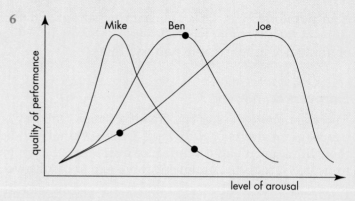

This graph shows the inverted U curves for three athletes, Mike, Ben and Joe. ● marks their positions on the curves.
a Who is giving the best performance?
b Who may be looking laid back or even bored?
c Who is probably trembling and sweating profusely?
d One is a snooker player, one a basketball player and one a weightlifter. Which is which? Explain your answer.

7 Some drugs are banned because they change the athlete's level of arousal. (See pages 106-109.)
a Name one banned drug that raises arousal levels.
b Name one banned drug that lowers arousal levels.
c For each drug, give two examples of sports where an athlete might use it to improve performance.

8 Copy and complete each statement using one term from this list. You must use a term once only:
an object   indirect aggression   direct aggression
aggressive attitude   jogging

a A rugby tackle is an example of _____ _____.
b An overhead smash in tennis is an example of _____ _____.
c There is not much obvious aggression in _____.
d In weightlifting, athletes direct their aggression against ____ ____.
e A runner's commitment to training, even in the cold and wet, shows an _____ _____.

9 People can be broadly divided into extroverts and introverts, depending on their behaviour.
a What qualities would you expect in an extrovert?
b What qualities would you expect in an introvert ?
c For each sport, say whether it is more likely to attract extroverts or introverts:
i football   ii skiing   iii sprinting   iv pot-holing
v netball   vi judo   vii orienteering   viii discus
d For which sports in c did you find it difficult to decide? Explain why.

Things to do

Goal setting

Setting goals can help you in all areas of life, not just sport. This shows a form for recording your goals and checking how well you met them.

```
My goals for: _____

Goal 1: _____
Goal 2: _____

How I did
Goal 1:    0  1  2  3  4  5  6  7  8  9  10
           Terrible        Good         Excellent

Goal 2:    0  1  2  3  4  5  6  7  8  9  10
           Terrible        Good         Excellent

Comment: _____
```

Try this out for different kinds of goals. For example:

a your next piece of homework. Your goals could be about the time you spend and the number of mistakes you make.

b your next sports training session.

Investigating arousal

1 a Choose one person from the class to be speaker. Allow the person to relax. Take his or her pulse for 15 seconds. Then send the person out of the room.

   b The class chooses a topic on which the speaker will make a speech. For example it could be a sport or a favourite TV programme.

   c Tell the speaker the topic. Allow five minutes to prepare the speech, which should last four minutes.

   d Take the speaker's pulse before the speech.

   e After the speech, take the speaker's pulse again.

   f What conclusions can you draw about the speaker's arousal level?

2 Choose someone who likes strong coffee but has not drunk any within the last 24 hours.

   a Take the person's pulse.

   b He or she now drinks a strong cup of coffee.

   c 20 minutes later, take the person's pulse again.

   d Has there been a change? Explain why.

3 This is to investigate the effect of an audience on arousal. You need two groups of five people to do wall squats, and a person to act as timer.

   a Group A does wall squats in private. The timer records how long each person holds the squat.

   b Group B does the same thing in front of the class, who watch quietly without any comment.

   c Which group does better? Can you explain why?

Investigating motivation

You will ask three groups of people to do standing broad jumps. Each group will need a start line marked on the floor, and someone with a tape to measure and record the jumps.

a Randomly choose three groups A, B and C, with 6 people in each group. Each person will do 3 jumps. The longest of the 3 will be recorded.

b Group A goes first. This group does the jumps in private, away from the class, and gets no feedback *of any kind*.

c Group B goes next. This group also works in private. But before starting the group is told that the two best performers will get a prize. Say what the prize is – for example a Mars bar.

d Group C goes last. The group jumps in front of the class. There is no prize, but the class is very encouraging and gives friendly and positive feedback. For example the class can cheer.

e The average jump for each group is calculated, by adding the 6 longest jumps and dividing by 6.

f Compare the results of the three groups. What do you notice? Explain it using the idea of motivation. Which kind of motivation worked best?

A relaxation technique

This method of relaxation is called **centering**.

1 Stand comfortably with your feet apart and your knees slightly bent.

2 Relax your face, neck, arm and shoulder muscles, until you feel all the tension has drained from them.

3 Still remaining relaxed, take a deep breath. Concentrate on your diaphragm. Move your chest as little as possible.

4 Now breathe out slowly and let yourself go. You will feel heavier as your muscles relax.

5 Practice this for just 1 minute a day for two weeks, in front of a mirror if possible.

Once you have learned this technique, you will be able to use it to calm down any time you feel nervous.

Visualization (mental rehearsal)

What is your next important event? It could be a sports event or an exam. Visualization will help you prepare.

1 Sit or lie down comfortably.

2 Close your eyes and breathe deeply until you feel really relaxed.

3 Now go through the event in your mind, step by step. Imagine you are in control and performing very well. Notice how you are feeling. Notice the different problems that arise and how well you deal with them.

Do this several times a day before the event. Think of all the problems that might arise and how you deal with each of them.

The technique is also useful when you are learning a new skill. You go through it lots of times in your mind, step by step.

12.1 Preventing injuries

Sports injuries can be very painful. They can ruin an athlete's career. Some can take years to heal properly. So avoid them if you can!

Two kinds of sports injuries

All sports injuries fall into two groups:

- injuries caused by a sudden stress on the body. For example a violent collision during football. Such injuries are common in contact sports like rugby and football.
- injuries which develop through overuse. Tennis players may suffer from tennis elbow and runners from an inflamed Achilles tendon. Overuse injuries can be brought on by heavy training programmes, insufficient rest between events, poor technique, or badly designed footwear or equipment.

A football injury. Injury like this, due to a collision or other sudden stress, is often described as **acute**. Injury due to overuse is described as **chronic**.

How you can avoid injury

Follow these ten rules to prevent injury to yourself and others.

1 Make sure you are fit for the activity.
The best way to prevent injury is be fit for your sport. If you are feeling ill, weak or in pain you should not take part in an event. If you do get injured, make sure you are fully recovered before you compete again.

2 Make sure you develop the right techniques.
For example a poor throwing technique for the javelin or discus will result in arm injury.

3 Play at the right level.
Choose a team which matches your physique and your level of skill. It would be dangerous for a fifteen-year-old rugby player to play scrum half with a senior team.

4 Know the rules for your sport and obey them.
Rules were developed to protect players as well to as test skills. In football, for example, you may not slide into tackles with studs up.

If you're a goal keeper in ice hockey, getting ready can take some time!

Warming up before a training session. As well as improving your performance it helps to protect you from injury.

In any sport involving throwing, good technique is vital to avoid injury to the arm or shoulder. In the javelin, it's also necessary to follow strict safety guidelines.

5 Make sure you are wearing the right kit.

If your sport requires protective gear such as mouth guards or shin guards, make sure you wear it. The correct footwear is especially important. Many injuries are due to poor footwear.
If you have long hair, tie it back. Do not wear a watch or jewellery that could catch in equipment or clothing. For sports such as wrestling and netball you must keep your fingernails short.

6 Make sure the equipment you use is in good repair.

For example make sure that rugby boots have no loose studs, that bouyancy aids have all their ties in place, and that gymnastics mats are in good condition.

7 Lift and carry equipment with care.

If you lift equipment the wrong way - for example windsurfing equipment or trampoline wings - you may find yourself injured before you even start! See page 37 for the correct way to lift things.

8 Watch out for hazards in the playing area.

For example broken glass on pitches, wet patches on floors, or rakes left lying in long jump pits. The weather can also be a hazard. Frost can make ground too hard. High winds and fog are hazards for canoeists, windsurfers and sailors.

9 Warm up correctly.

Many injuries such as sprains and pulled muscles can be avoided by warming up correctly. See page 94 for the right way to warm up.

10 Cool down correctly.

The cool down helps to prevent stiffness and soreness. That means you are better prepared for the next event. See page 94 for more.

Questions

1 Give two examples of sports where:
  a people are grouped according to age
  b people are grouped according to weight
  Why is this done?

2 Why is it better to join a team that matches your skill level? Give as many reasons as you can.

3 What protective gear is used in these sports?
  a windsurfing   b boxing   c baseball

4 What steps could you take to reduce the risk of injury in:
  a canoeing?   b swimming?
  c dance?   d tennis?

12.2 Emergency action (1)

What do you do if an ill or injured person collapses in front of you? Following the **DRABC** routine could save a life.

The aim of DRABC is to keep the person breathing until an ambulance arrives. Because, without oxygen, the brain is damaged within just three or four minutes and dead within ten.

D is for Danger
- First, stop and check for danger before you rush to help a **casualty** (injured person). There could be danger from equipment, falling masonry, electricity, gas, fire or fumes.
- If there is danger, do *not* put yourself at risk. **Your own safety comes first.** Shout or phone for help.
- If there is no danger, clear the area around the casualty. This could mean stopping a game.

R is for Response
- Shake the casualty gently by the shoulders and shout 'Can you hear me?'
- If the casualty shows any response, he or she is **conscious**. You can tell from the response how weak the casualty is.
- If the casualty can speak, find out if and where he or she has pain. Do what you can to stop the casualty's condition from getting worse. For example stop severe bleeding and support broken bones (pages 138-141). Send for an ambulance, if necessary, as soon as possible.
- If there is no response the casualty is **unconscious**. This is very serious. Move on to **resuscitation** (A, B and C).

A is for Airway
When a person is unconscious, the tongue can block the airway. Preventing this is the most important thing you can do.

- Loosen any tight clothing.
- Raise the chin and tilt the head back to open the airway fully.
- Remove any obvious obstruction such as a gum shield. Use a tissue round your fingers to scrape away any vomit.

> *Reassuring the casualty*
> - The casualty is probably scared as well as in pain.
> - So reassure the casualty. Explain what you are doing. Say that help is on the way.
> - Do this even if he or she is unconscious.
> - Speak calmly and quietly.
> - Do not pass your anxiety onto the casualty.

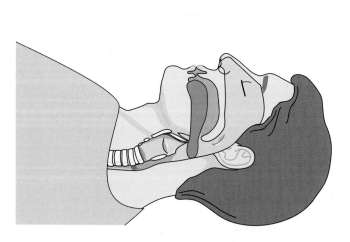

Tongue blocking the airway in an unconscious person.

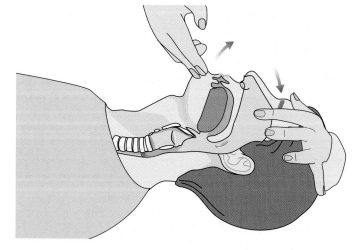

Raise chin and tilt head back to unblock the airway.

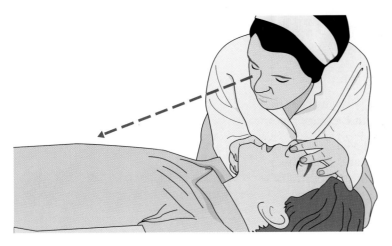

Looking, listening and feeling for breathing.

The best preparation you can make for dealing with an emergency is to take a First Aid course with the British Red Cross or St John.

B is for Breathing

Is the casualty breathing?

- **Look** for the chest rising and falling. **Listen** for breathing sounds. **Feel** for breath on your cheek. Moistening the cheek will help.
- If the casualty is breathing, do what you can to stop severe bleeding and support broken bones (pages 138-141).
- Then place the casualty in the **recovery position** (page 137) while you get help.
- But if the casualty shows no signs of breathing, move on to C.

C is for Circulation

- Feel for the **carotid** pulse, below the ear, at either side of the Adam's apple (page 58).
- A pulse shows the heart is beating and the blood circulating. So you need to give **mouth-to-mouth ventilation** (the kiss of life) to restore breathing.
- If there is no pulse you need to give both **cardiac massage** *and* **mouth-to-mouth ventilation**, to restore circulation and breathing. You can find out about these in the next Unit.

Calling for help

- Dial 999. The emergency operator will ask you:
  - which service you want (police, fire or ambulance)
  - what your phone number is, in case you get cut off.
- You may have to wait to get through to the ambulance service. Do not hang up!
- When you get through, be ready to explain:
  - *exactly* where the casualty is. Clear directions save vital time.
  - the nature of the injuries, as far as you can tell.
  This information will help the ambulance staff to prepare.

In an emergency, if you're on your own, it may be wiser to phone for help *before* you try to help the casualty. You need to stay calm and decide how urgently help is needed.

Questions

1 What does DRABC stand for?
2 Why is it important to check for danger before you rush to help a casualty?
3 How can you tell if a person is unconscious?

4 How do you ensure an airway is open?
5 How should you check for breathing?
6 Why do you think it is better to check the carotid pulse than the radial pulse, in a casualty?

12.3 Emergency action (II)

Mouth-to-mouth ventilation

In **mouth-to-mouth ventilation**, you force air from your lungs into the casualty's lungs. The oxygen in this air can keep the casualty alive.

1 Make sure the casualty's airway is fully open (page 134).
2 Pinch the casualty's nostrils closed with your thumb and first finger.
3 Take a deep breath. Then seal your lips firmly around the casualty's open mouth. Breathe out smoothly and firmly until you see the casualty's chest rise, as shown below.

 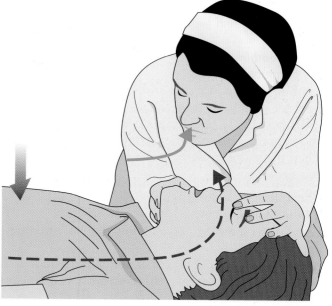

4 Take your mouth away and breathe in. The chest will fall.
5 Repeat with 1 breath every 6 seconds, for one minute.
6 If breathing has not returned within a minute, phone 999 for an ambulance. Get back to the casualty as quickly as you can.
7 Continue mouth-to-mouth ventilation until breathing returns or help arrives. Check the pulse at the end of each minute.
   Be prepared to do cardiac massage if the pulse disappears.
8 If breathing returns to normal, place the casualty in the recovery position.

Cardiac massage

Cardiac arrest is when your heart stops beating, for example during a heart attack. When it stops the circulation and pulse stop too.

Cardiac massage or **external chest compression** is a way of squeezing the heart so that blood is forced out of it and round the body. It must be combined with mouth-to-mouth ventilation so that the blood gets oxygen too.

Cardiac massage probably won't start the heart beating properly. A special machine called a **fibrillator** is usually needed for that. But it can keep the casualty alive until the machine arrives.

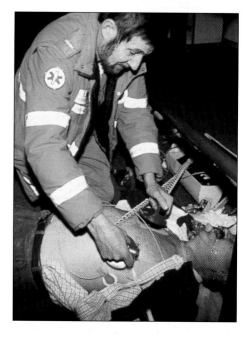

An ambulance man using a fibrillator on a heart-attack victim.

How to do cardiac massage

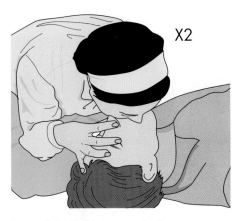
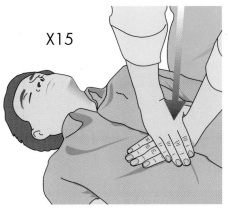
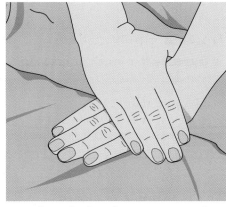

X2

X15

Note how the hands are positioned.

1 Dial 999 for an ambulance.
2 Make sure the casualty's airway is open.
3 Start with 2 breaths of mouth-to-mouth ventilation.
4 Now use your weight to compress the chest 15 times as shown.
   Do it smoothly and quickly, a bit faster than once per second.
5 Next give 2 more mouth-to-mouth ventilations.
6 Repeat the pattern of 15 compressions and 2 ventilations until help
   arrives. Don't stop unless the casualty's condition improves. (Skin
   colour may improve or the casualty may move.) Check the pulse.
7 Continue with mouth-to-mouth ventilation if necessary.
   Check the pulse every minute.
8 If breathing also restarts, place the casualty in the recovery position.
   Check the breathing and pulse every three minutes.

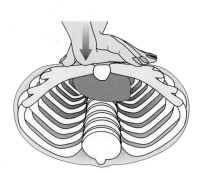

The recovery position

It is the safest position for an unconscious breathing person.

The head is tilted so that the tongue can't block the throat. Since the head is a little lower than the rest of the body, vomit will drain from the mouth and not choke the person.

You can safely leave an unconscious person in this position while you get help.

For instructions on the recovery position, see the activity on page 145.

Questions

1 Give another name for mouth-to-mouth ventilation.
2 How does mouth-to-mouth ventilation work?
3 What does *cardiac arrest* mean?
4 How does cardiac massage work?

5 Explain why mouth-to-mouth ventilation is always combined with cardiac massage.
6 Explain why the recovery position is a safe position for an unconscious breathing person.

12.4 Bone and joint injuries

Fractures

A **fracture** is a break or crack in a bone.

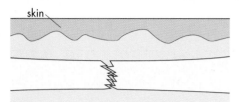

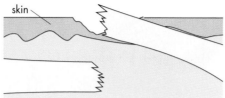

This is a **simple** or **closed** fracture. The bone is cracked but the skin is not damaged.

This is an **open** or **compound** fracture. The skin is damaged and the bone may stick out.

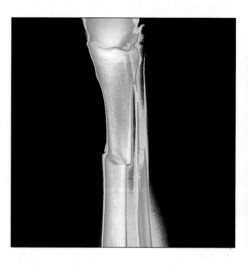

An X-ray showing a closed fracture of the tibia or shinbone. (Colour has been added to show up the fracture more clearly.)

Since bones contain nerves and blood vessels, a fracture brings pain and bleeding. Bleeding in turn leads to **swelling** and **bruising** when the blood leaks into the surrounding tissue.

Signs and symptoms
- The casualty may have heard or felt a snap.
- There is pain and tenderness around the injury. Moving makes it worse.
- The casualty will not be able to move the part normally.
- The bleeding leads to swelling. Bruising develops later.
- The limb may look deformed. For example a foot may be twisted backwards. To check, compare the two limbs.
- There may be a grating noise when the parts of the cracked bone rub against each other. But don't try to test for this!

What you can do
- Dial 999 for an ambulance.
- Do *not* move the casualty and do *not* try to straighten the fractured limb, since this will make the damage worse.
- Support the limb *above and below the fracture* using towels, cushions or folded clothing.
- If the fracture is in an arm bone, a sling made of a towel, bandage or T-shirt can be used for support. But be very careful!

Dislocation

This is where a bone is pulled out of its normal position at a joint. It is usually caused by violent twisting. It usually happens at the shoulder, elbow, finger, thumb and ankle joints. Dislocation and fracture often go together. If in doubt, treat as a fracture.

Signs and symptoms
- There is severe pain at or near the joint.
- The joint appears deformed and the casualty can't move it.
- There is swelling, and bruising appears later.

What you can do
- Dial 999 for an ambulance.
- Support the injured part using clothing, towels or cushions.
- Support injured elbow or finger joints with slings or bandages.

Sprain

A **sprain** occurs when a ligament at a joint gets stretched and torn. Twisting your foot when running can give you a sprained ankle. Some sprains are minor. But in a severe sprain the ligament is badly torn and the injury looks like a fracture. If in doubt, treat it as a fracture.

Signs and symptoms
- There is pain and tenderness around the joint, and movement makes it worse.
- Swelling appears around the joint, followed later by bruising.

What you can do
- If in doubt, follow the instructions for a fracture.
- For minor sprains follow the **RICE** routine below.

RICE

When bones, joints, ligaments, muscles or tendons get damaged, the blood vessels around them get damaged too. Blood leaks into the surrounding tissue. This causes swelling, pain and bruising, and slows down healing. So the aim of RICE is to stop the blood leaking.

- **R**est. Movement keeps the blood leaking. So stay still.
- **I**ce. Place an icepack around the injured part for 30 minutes or so. Cold makes blood vessels constrict and this reduces bleeding.
- **C**ompression. Bandage the injured part firmly but not tightly, using a crepe bandage. This reduces bleeding.
- **E**levate the injured limb. This reduces blood flow to the limb because the blood has to flow against gravity.

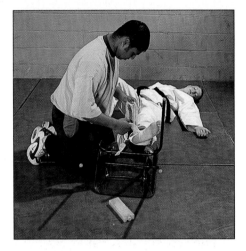

RICE treatment under way. To elevate the injured limb use whatever support is available.

Torn knee cartilage

Your knee joint has two special curved pads of cartilage. These may tear when the knee is twisted violently. This is called **torn cartilage**.

Signs and symptoms
- There is pain on one side of the knee joint.
- The joint may 'lock' and not straighten fully for a time.
- It may swell later that day or next morning.

What you can do
- Use an icepack to reduce the swelling.
- Get the athlete to the doctor.

Torn cartilage cannot be properly repaired. The athlete must drop out of sport, or have surgery to replace the cartilage with artificial material. Surgery cannot make the joint as good as it was before the injury.

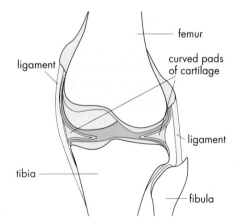

The cartilage pads in the knee

Questions

1 Describe two different kinds of fracture.
2 Give four signs and symptoms of a fracture.
3 What is: **a** a dislocation? **b** a sprain?
4 **a** What is RICE? **b** What is it used for, and why?

12.5 Muscle and skin damage

Strained or pulled muscles

A **strain** or **pull** is a tear in a muscle or its tendon, caused by violent over-stretching. It often happens with hamstrings and calf muscles, especially if you don't warm up properly. The Achilles tendon of the calf muscle (gastrocnemius) can tear completely. That is very painful.

Signs and symptoms
- A sudden sharp pain at the site of the injury.
- This is followed by swelling, stiffness and sometimes cramp.
- A casualty with a torn Achilles tendon will collapse to the ground and be unable to get up again.

What you can do
- For minor strains follow the **RICE** routine (page 139).
- A casualty with a serious strain must be brought to hospital.

Tennis and golfer's elbow

These are muscle injuries caused by overuse of muscles in the lower arm. In **tennis elbow** the area around the outer bony bump on the elbow is inflamed, tender and painful. This injury can occur in fishing as well as racket sports. In **golfer's elbow** the area around the inner bony bump is affected.

What you can do
- If the injury is very painful, an icepack will help.
- The elbow must be rested until it recovers, which could take weeks.
- The usual treatment is physiotherapy and injection of a steroid into the muscle.

Cramp

Cramp occurs when muscle fibres fail to relax and their blood supply is cut off. This causes pain. It usually happens when muscles are tired, or when you have lost a lot of salt through sweating.

What you can do
- Stretch the muscle slowly and gently. Hold the stretch.
- When the muscle has relaxed, massage it very gently.

Stitch

This is a small sharp pain in your side or upper abdomen. You get it during vigorous exercise. It may be caused by exercising too soon after eating. Stop exercising for a short time and it will go.

Winded

A blow to the abdomen from a ball, elbow or knee can leave you 'winded'. You can't breathe in or out. This is because your diaphragm has stopped working.

What you can do
- Relax. You will normally recover within a few minutes.

Powerful repetitious movements in any sport can lead to overuse injury. For golfers, it's golfer's elbow!

Cuts

The secret of treating a cut is to stop the bleeding and let the blood clot as quickly as possible.

- Cover the cut with a clean pad or cloth and press down firmly on it to stop the bleeding. Use plastic or rubber gloves if you can. (Why?)
- Lie the casualty down and raise the injured part, to reduce blood flow to it.
- Continue to apply pressure until bleeding stops. For a bad cut this could take 15 minutes or more.
- If blood seeps through the pad, do not remove it. (Why?) Just put another one on top.
- When bleeding stops, tie the pad firmly but not tightly in place using a bandage, scarf or tie.
- If bleeding is severe, dial 999 for an ambulance. The casualty will probably need stitches.

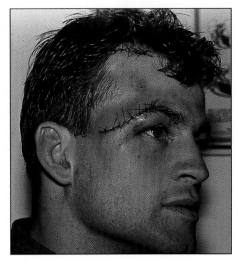

The England player Jon Callard needed 20 stitches after an opponent stamped on his face during a rugby international.

Bruises

If you fall hard during a game, or crash into an opponent, you'll probably get bruised. Bruises are caused by blood leaking from damaged blood vessels under the skin.

Signs and symptoms
- First there is pain and swelling in the bruised area.
- Then the skin discolours. It goes mottled blue and yellow.

What you can do
The treatment is part of the RICE routine.

- Apply an icepack or cold compress to the bruised area to reduce the blood leakage.
- For serious bruising, compression with a crepe bandage will help.

Abrasions

Abrasions or **grazes** occur when skin is scraped off your body. For example during a sliding tackle on a hard pitch, or a fall on gravel.

What you can do
- If the wound is dirty, clean it gently with tepid water.
- If it is bleeding a little, just let the blood clot.
- Allow the wound to dry naturally if possible. But if there is danger of infection, cover it with a plaster.

Questions

1 What is a *strain*? How could you prevent it?
2 Explain how to treat a strain.
3 How would you treat cramp in your calf muscle?

4 What is *tennis elbow*? What is the treatment for it?
5 Describe the steps to take in treating a bad cut.
6 Explain why bruises form when you get hit or fall.

12.6 Some dangerous conditions

Concussion

Concussion results from injury to the brain. It is caused by a knock on the head which shakes the brain around.

Signs and symptoms
The casualty may :

- become unconscious. This could last from seconds to hours.
- feel sick, dizzy or drowsy.
- get confused, stare and suffer memory loss.

These signs may not appear until hours after the injury.

What to do
- Place an unconscious casualty in the recovery position. Dial 999.
- A player who's been knocked unconscious, even briefly, should be kept under medical observation for at least twenty four hours.

Shock

Shock is when there is not enough blood circulating round your body. It may be caused by:

- fluid loss. For example from severe bleeding or burns, vomiting, diarrhoea, or heavy sweating.
- severe pain, when blood is diverted to the painful part.

Signs and symptoms
- The skin is cold, grey and clammy. The lips may be blue.
- The pulse is rapid and weak, and breathing rapid and shallow.
- The casualty feels dizzy, thirsty, and may try to vomit.
- The casualty feels anxious and panicky.
- If fluid loss continues the casualty becomes unconscious and dies.

What to do
- Dial 999 for an ambulance.
- If the casualty is bleeding do what you can to stop it (page 141).
- Place the casualty in the recovery position.
- Reassure the casualty. Shock is very frightening.

Hypothermia (freezing)

Hypothermia means your core body temperature has fallen below about 35 °C. Your body is too cold to function properly. This could happen if you have been out in the cold, wet and wind for too long and you are very tired. For example when sailing or climbing.

Signs and symptoms
- The casualty starts to act strangely. For example he or she may become aggressive, dreamy or apathetic.
- The casualty's skin is cold and pale, and breathing is shallow.
- The casualty is weak, stumbles a lot, and has an overwhelming urge to lie down and rest.
- He or she may collapse, become unconscious and die if not treated.

> *Don't ...*
>
> - Don't ever give a shock victim anything to drink – or eat. Not even a glass of water.
> - Don't cover the victim with lots of blankets so that he or she gets too warm.
>
> These actions divert blood to the gut or skin, away from vital organs.
>
> But it's okay to cover the victim up to keep him or her close to normal body temperature.

A sea rescue. Sea-rescue teams have plenty of experience in detecting and treating hypothermia.

Treatment
- If possible bring the casualty indoors or to a shelter. Replace damp clothes by warm dry ones and let the casualty rest.
- A conscious recovering casualty can be put in a hot bath.
- Give hot sweet drinks if available, but *no alcohol*.
- If shelter is not possible, protect the casualty by covering damp clothes with dry clothes or sleeping bags, and a polythene sheet.
- Lie the casualty down on blankets or other insulation.
- If the casualty's condition gets worse, send for help.

Hyperthermia (overheating)

Hyperthermia means your body temperature has risen above 39 °C. This can lead to several different conditions.

Heat exhaustion When your temperature rises you sweat a lot. If you lose too much water and salts by sweating, you get heat exhaustion.

Signs and symptoms
- The skin is pale, grey and clammy.
- The pulse is weak and rapid.
- The person may feel weak and dizzy and get cramps and headache.
- If water loss is severe, shock may develop.

What you should do
- Lie the casualty down in a cool place, with legs raised.
- Give him or her frequent sips of a weak solution of salt in water.
- Call a doctor for further advice.

Dehydration This is like heat exhaustion but less severe. The casualty feels weak and dizzy. Give plenty of water to drink.

Heat stroke This is when your body suddenly loses its ability to sweat and your temperature rises out of control. It usually happens during long, vigorous exercise on a hot and humid day.

Signs and symptoms
1 The casualty suddenly lapses into confusion or delirium.
2 The casualty is flushed, with a rapid strong pulse and hot dry skin.
3 He or she may become unconscious and die if not treated quickly.

What to do
- Lie the casualty down in a cool breezy place. Remove outer clothing and wrap the casualty in a cold wet sheet. Keep the sheet saturated with cold water and fan it as much as possible.
- Continue until the casualty has cooled down.
- Call a doctor for further advice.

In hot weather, players need plenty of liquid to avoid dehydration.

Questions

1 What causes concussion? How should you treat it?
2 What is *shock*? List four signs of shock.
3 How would you treat hypothermia?
4 Explain what heat stroke is and how to treat it.

Questions on Chapter 12

1 Two kinds of injuries occur in sport.
   a What are they called?
   b Give two examples of each, and say how they might occur.

2 Explain why these are important in preventing injury:
   a the warm up   b the cool down

3 Give as many reasons as you can why it is essential to keep to the rules in sport, and obey the umpire or referee.

4 Explain the reason for each of these rules.
   a No jewellery can be worn during a match, apart from a wedding ring taped to the finger. (Netball)
   b In certain weather conditions, the length of a match can be decided by the country concerned. (Netball)
   c After taking a corner, if the attacking team's first shot is a hit it must be no higher than the backboard. (Hockey)
   d As soon as a scrum collapses, play must stop. (Rugby)
   e Shin pads must be worn. (Football)
   f One bouncer per batsman per over is allowed. (Cricket)
   g If you commit five fouls you will be sent off. (Basketball)
   h If the umpire sees you bleeding, you will be sent off to cover or stop the bleeding. (Netball, rugby and other sports)

5 For each activity list the likely hazards, including hazards to onlookers.

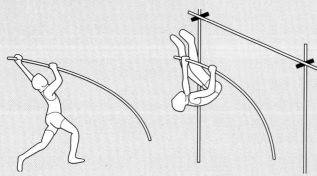

   a pole vaulting

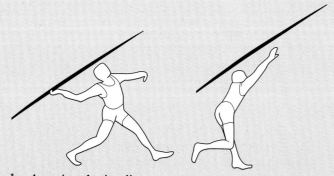

   b throwing the javelin

6

   a Which features of this rugby boot help the player to play safely?
   b Which feature(s) could be a danger to both the player and his opponent? How?
   c Can you see anything about the shape that leaves the player open to injury?
   d How would you improve the design of rugby boots?

7

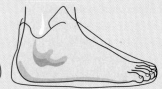

The tennis shoe on the left is too big. The one on the right is too small. Say what problems each could cause the player. Think of as many as you can.

8 Below is a list of common injuries for some different sports. See if you can match the injury to the sport.

A blisters on hands and buttocks
B dislocation of finger joints
C permanently slurred speech and memory loss
D 'grass' burns
E sprains of the wrist
F an inflamed Achilles tendon
G inflammation around the elbow joint

i soccer
ii boxing
iii tennis
iv rowing
v basketball
vi distance running
vii shot putting

9 This list shows the parts of the body injured in rugby:

	% of all rugby injuries
lower limb and ankle	33.1
head and neck	24.0
shoulder	13.0
trunk	11.0
knee	9.9
arms	9.0

Find out what steps are taken (if any) to protect these different parts of the body in rugby.

10 Analyse the risks in *your* sport. List:
   a the parts of the body most likely to be injured
   b hazards that could arise from equipment
   c possible danger to onlookers
   d rules that are designed to prevent injury
   e protective kit or materials used in the sport

11 Match each condition **i - vii** with a letter **A - H**.
   You may need to use a letter more than once.

   A   sprain
   B   strain
   C   fracture
   D   cramp
   E   abrasion
   F   pain and swelling
   G   bruising
   H   dislocation

   i   muscle 'stuck' in contraction
   ii   damaged skin
   iii   tear in muscle or tendon
   iv   bone out of position at a joint
   v   torn ligament at a joint
   vi   crack in a bone
   vii   blood leaking from damaged blood vessels

12 You are in the middle of a hockey match. The centre
   forward and goal keeper have just collided at speed.
   The centre forward is lying still with her eyes closed.
   a Explain how you would deal with this situation using
      the DRABC principle.
   b Once she comes to, for what else might the centre
      forward need treatment ?

13 Match each condition **i - x** with a treatment **A - I**.
   You may choose more than one treatment if necessary.

   A   RICE
   B   support around injured part, move as little as possible
   C   rest, shelter and insulation
   D   wrap in wet sheet in breezy area
   E   hot sweet drink
   F   elevation and direct pressure using a clean pad or
       cloth
   G   recovery position and reassurance until help arrives
   H   ice pack
   I   DRABC

   i   someone about to drown
   ii   hypothermia
   ii   heat stroke
   iv   a large gash on the leg
   v   bruising above the eye from a blow
   vi   sprained ankle
   vii   shock
   viii fracture of the collar bone
   ix   heart attack
   x   tear in a calf muscle

Things to do

Placing a casualty in the recovery position

Below are the instructions for placing a casualty in the
recovery position. Work with two partners.
a One person acts as casualty. The second reads out the
   instructions. The third carries them out.
b Switch roles and repeat.
c Switch roles again. But this time the instructions are
   not read aloud. Instead the reader checks that the job
   is being done properly.

1 With the casualty lying on his back, tilt the head back
   and chin up to open the airway.
2 Straighten the legs.
3 Move the arm nearest you so that it looks like the arm
   of a policeman stopping traffic.

4 Bring the other arm across the chest. Arrange so that
   the casualty's cheek rests on the back of this hand.
   Keep your hand on this hand for step 5.

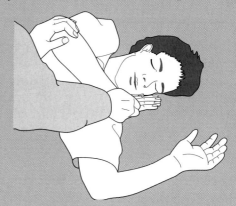

5 With your other hand, reach across the casualty's far
   leg. Lift it so that the knee bends to a right angle.
   Then pull it to roll the casualty towards you.

6 Once the casualty is on his side, gently tilt the head
   back to keep the airway open. Use his hand under the
   cheek to hold it like that.
7 Compare the result with the photo on page 137.

13.1 Leisure, recreation and sport

What do you do in your spare time? Why do you do it? How does it affect your health and fitness?

Leisure

Leisure is how you spend your free time, when you can do as you please. Perhaps you like to watch TV, or play computer games, or abseil down a cliff face.

What you choose to do will depend on your culture and upbringing, your social class, and the facilities available. For example most homes have a TV, but you need to be rich or have rich friends to play polo.

The growth in leisure

As a society, we have more and more time for leisure. (You may not have noticed!) There are several reasons for this:

- Improvements in technology mean that machines are taking over more of our work. This leaves more people unemployed or in part-time work, or forced to take early retirement.
- Labour-saving devices also cut the time for household chores.
- Improvements in health care and the standard of living means we are living longer. The number of healthy, active, retired people is increasing.
- Some people choose to work less, to reduce the stress in their lives. Some choose to **job-share** with another person.

Sadly, it is unemployed people who have most leisure time – and they'd rather be working. For full-time workers, the average working week is in fact getting longer, not shorter. This is partly because employers offer overtime to existing workers, rather than take on new ones, and partly because people are less secure in their jobs and feel they must work harder.

Increased leisure is a challenge to the government which must provide **facilities** for leisure: parks, playing fields, swimming pools and so on.

It is also a challenge to the **leisure industry** which provides holidays, theme parks, bowling alleys, ice rinks, cinemas, theatres, rock concerts and fitness centres, with the aim of making a **profit**.

Recreation

Recreation is any activity you do voluntarily, in your leisure time, for pleasure and enjoyment. It's a form of play.

During recreation you can forget about your problems. You can recharge your batteries or **re-create** yourself. You feel refreshed, and more able to face life's pressures and stresses.

Physical recreation is where you choose a physical activity. For example rollerblading, cycling, football or swimming. It does not include serious sporting activity. If you play for Manchester United, that counts as sport.

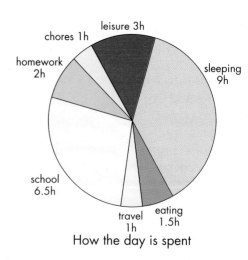

How the day is spent

Top six physical activities for 16 - 19 age group (1993 - 94)	
Activity	**% participating**
Males	
snooker/ pool/billiards	56
walking	45
football	44
cycling	37
swimming	23
golf	15
Females	
walking	40
keep fit/yoga	29
swimming	26
snooker/ pool/billiards	26
cycling	14
tenpin bowls/ skittles	9

Why choose physical recreation?

There are lots of good reasons for taking up a physical activity.
They fall into three groups:

- **Health.** You might take up jogging or swimming for health reasons.
  As you saw in Unit 1.1, exercise helps to prevent illness and relieve
  stress. It helps to improve your shape. You look and feel better and
  will probably live longer.
- **The activity itself.** You might go sailing or scuba diving or jazz
  dancing just because you love it.
- **Social reasons.** Taking up a physical activity often means joining
  a club or team. This gives you the chance to meet new people and
  make new friends. Activities such as skiing and sailing can be very
  sociable. Some business people use golf as a good way to entertain
  their contacts.

Good for your health – and fun!

Where does sport fit in?

When does your swimming stop being recreation and turn into sport?
Sport has these characteristics:

- It is **institutionalised** and **competitive**. That means there are
  organized events with rules and regulations, and you set out to win.
- It requires vigorous physical exertion and/or the use of complex skills.
  Lazing in the pool on your back does not count.
- The player is motivated by a mixture of satisfaction and **extrinsic**
  factors (page 124). For example payment or a prize.

You can show physical recreation and sport on a continuum like this:

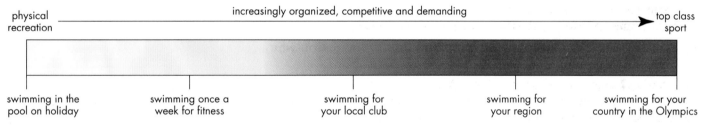

physical recreation — increasingly organized, competitive and demanding → top class sport

| swimming in the pool on holiday | swimming once a week for fitness | swimming for your local club | swimming for your region | swimming for your country in the Olympics |

Note that serious athletes are divided into **amateurs**, who do not get
paid for playing sport, and **professionals** who do. You can find out
more about amateurs and professionals in Unit 15.1.

Questions

1 What is *leisure*?
2 Does PE in school count as recreation? Why?
3 Give two examples of a recreational activity that is:
  a physical **b** not physical
4 We have an increasing amount of leisure. Why?
5 There are three kinds of reason for participating in
  physical recreation. What are they? Give examples.

6 Explain why a friendly game of tennis after school is
  recreation rather than sport.
7 Look at the table of physical activities opposite.
  a Overall, which sex participates more?
    Why do you think this is?
  b Yoga and keep fit do not appear in the top six for
    males. Why do you think this is?

13.2 Factors affecting participation

What encourages people to take up a physical activity? What makes one activity more popular than another? There are many factors at work.

Age
People take part less in physical recreation and sport as they get older. It also depends on the activity. For gymnastics you need to be young and flexible. Golf depends more on skill than on strength or speed, so you can play at 16 or 60. Walking and swimming also appeal to all ages. Crown green bowling is more popular among older people.

Sex
Fewer females than males take part in physical activities, as you can see from the table on the right. Why do you think this is?
There is more about participation by women in Unit 15.4.

Education
Your education has a big effect on your attitude to sport and physical recreation. If your school is keen on sport you probably play a lot already. If you enjoy it at school you are likely to continue later.

Tradition and culture
Tradition and culture also affect participation. For example:

- some nations have a strong tradition of a particular sport. The West Indies has a tradition of cricket, and America of baseball. Kabaddi is popular in parts of Asia.
- most sports were originally men only. Women had to fight their way in.
- some cultures disapprove of women taking part in physical recreation in public, or in mixed company. This is one reason why gyms and swimming pools have 'women only' sessions.

Peer-group pressure
Your **peer group** means the people you associate with who have similar backgrounds and interests and are around your own age.

Your peer group puts pressure on you to behave in a certain way. This is not always expressed in words. If you wear the wrong clothes or do the wrong things you may feel left out. If your peer group approves of an activity, that will encourage you to do it. Sadly, peer-group pressure often forces people to give up sports they enjoy.

Family
We pick up many of our habits and values from home. If a parent or older brother or sister enjoys sport and encourages you, you are more likely to participate. Most young people depend on a parent for money for kit and help with travel to sports events.

Economics
Activities like sailing, golf and riding can be expensive. You may be unable to afford them. In the same way sports facilities are expensive to build and a city, area or country may be unable to afford them.

Unemployed people are in a difficult situation: plenty of time to fill but not much money. To encourage them, sports facilities often charge the unemployed less, especially at quiet times of day.

% participating in one or more physical activities (including walking)

Year	Male	Female
1987	70	52
1990	73	57
1993	72	57

Physical activities and social class

% participating, 1993/94

	Professional [a]	Skilled manual [b]
Walking	57	39
Snooker/pool/billiards	11	17
Darts	6	8
Golf	9	6
Running/jogging	11	3

[a] jobs like doctor and solicitor
[b] jobs like plumber and electrician

Access

You may not have access to a particular sport because the nearest facilities are miles away, or even abroad.

Disability

A disability may restrict your activities. But many sports have changed the rules to suit disabled people, and set up coaching and competitions for them. Modern sports facilities have wheelchair ramps, lifts and special changing rooms for disabled people.

Environment and climate

The activities on offer also depend on the environment and climate. If you live near the sea or a lake you may have the chance to windsurf or sail. You may want to go abroad for downhill or cross-country skiing, or to try sports like scuba diving.

The media

The media play a big part in making a sport popular. During Wimbledon, people rush out to play tennis. American football is growing more popular in the UK every year, thanks mainly to TV.

Sports can also go out of fashion. Snooker and squash are less popular than in the 1980s. There was a craze in the 1980s for BMX bikes, and tracks were built around the country. But the craze didn't last for long.

You can find out more about sport and the media on pages 180–183.

Politics

The extent to which people take part in a physical activity also depends on their politicians! All governments get involved in sport for one reason or another. For example:

- Facilities cost so much to build that the government usually has to pay at least something towards them.
- A government may promote sport for all in an attempt to cut the cost of the health service, or cut crime.
- It may promote excellence in sport so as to bring a sense of pride to the country and raise its standing in the outside world.

In the UK, the government aims to promote wide participation *and* excellence in sport. It is particularly keen on sport in schools. You can find out more about this in Unit 13.5.

It's important for all age groups to have access to an activity they enjoy. Bowls has always been popular among older people.

Questions

1 Give two examples of a physical recreation that:
   a people tend to give up in their forties or earlier
   b you could carry on into old age
2 Name two sports that have traditionally been popular in the UK.
3 a What is a *peer group*?
   b Give an example from real life to show how a peer group can influence a choice of activity.

4 Do the activities people choose depend at all on social class? Give examples.
5 Explain how money can affect participation in a sport for: a an individual b a country
6 Think of two examples of recreational activities that are fashionable right now.
7 Why might putting money into sport help to cut the cost of the health service?

13.3 Facilities

Some facilities for sport and recreation are **built**. Examples are tennis courts, swimming pools, running tracks, gyms, and reservoirs used as water sports centres.

Others are **natural**: lakes, rivers, the sea, hills, forests and mountains. But even these must be planned and looked after. They may need car parks, rubbish bins, marked footpaths, toilets and information centres. They may need areas marked out for different use. For example fishing and water skiing don't go together. Why?

Who provides facilities?

Local authorities. Your local council probably owns most of the local sports facilities: playing fields, tennis courts, pitch and putt, swimming pools and so on.

But it does not necessarily run them. By law it must allow different companies to compete or **tender** for the chance to run them. This is called **compulsory competitive tendering**. The council provides the budget and spells out its requirements. For example it may set out the prices users should be charged. The company who offers the best service within the budget will win the contract.

Most schools and their facilities are owned by the local education authority. Some school facilities are **dual purpose** - they are also used by local people in the evenings. This way they get maximum use, and the links between the school and community are strengthened.

Private enterprise. Many facilities are set up and run by business in order to make profit. For example:

- private gyms and golf clubs. Some are attached to hotels but also open to the locals. Some are very exclusive and membership may cost thousands of pounds a year.
- theme parks such as Alton Towers.
- holiday facilities such as Center Parcs.

Voluntary organizations. These are bodies set up to meet a need rather than make a profit. There are lots of them, including:

- local youth clubs, Scouts and Guides
- churches
- large national charities such as The Royal Society for the Protection of Birds, The National Trust and the Youth Hostel Association.

All these provide recreational facilities. For example the National Trust owns stately homes, gardens, farms, woodland and nature reserves which it opens to the public. Local churches may offer church halls for activities such as yoga and aerobics classes.

The Sports Council. This body was set up by the government. It runs national facilities which are centres of excellence, mainly for use by top class athletes. You can find out more about these on page 156.

The Sports Council also helps other organizations with advice and grants for sport facilities. See Units 13.4 and 14.4 for more.

Some facilities are fairly evenly spread. Others aren't. Where's your nearest water-skiing facility?

The location of facilities

Where are facilities located? It depends on several factors:

- **Population.** There is no point building a leisure centre miles from anywhere, with no one to use it. You will lose money on the venture. Most facilities are built in or near towns and cities.
- **The natural environment.** Canoeing and sailing clubs need to be beside water. Facilities for climbers need to be close to the mountains.
- **Cost.** Land is more expensive in some areas than others. A developer may be forced to choose a cheaper area. Even in a cheaper area, a local council may be unable to afford new facilities. But there are ways round this. It could qualify for a grant from the government or the EU, or for a Lottery Sports Fund award.
- **Access.** A facility must be easy to get to, especially if it's out of town. That means close to good roads and within reach of public transport.
- **Planning permission.** Every facility needs planning permission from the local authority. Local people get a chance to express their views. They may object to a facility that will 'spoil' a beauty spot, or bring more noise and traffic to the area.

Meeting the users' needs

Some facilities cater for just one activity. Some cater for many. Some are designed for top athletes. Some are for the general user. Think of all the groups who might use the local swimming pool: mums with toddlers, families, young adults, school and evening classes, the local swimming club, and disabled, elderly and unemployed people.

You must consider all the users when designing the facility, and when deciding on timetables, charges and opening hours.

Questions

1 Find two local examples of a recreational facility:
   a which is owned by the local council
   b which is privately owned
   c which is provided by a voluntary organization.

2 A local gym may need to cater for several different groups of users. List as many as you can.

3 How might a swimming pool cater for disabled people? Think of as many ways as you can.

13.4 Sport for all?

Sport and physical recreation are good for us. That's why the government has been trying for years to get more of us to take part. It has worked mainly through the **Sports Council**.

The Sports Council

In fact there are five separate Sports Councils: one each for England, Scotland, Wales and Northern Ireland, plus a United Kingdom Sports Council. They are funded mainly by the government. They were first set up in 1972 with these aims:

- to increase participation in sport and physical recreation
- to increase the number and quality of facilities
- to develop excellence in sport.

These are big aims. To achieve them, the Council had to:

- collect the facts - for example about which groups of people don't take part in physical recreation, and which areas have poor facilities
- set goals to improve the situation
- take action to achieve those goals.

Examples of goals

The Sports Council goals are set out in policy papers which appear from time to time. For example in 1988 a paper called **Into The Nineties** set out goals to be achieved by 1993. These included:

- to encourage an extra 1.25 million women and 750 000 men to take part in sport
- to target in particular the young, women, the unemployed, the disabled and ethnic minorities
- to provide 500 more sports halls and 150 more swimming pools.

Campaigns

To encourage people to join in physical activities, the Sports Council ran campaigns aimed at different target groups. The hope was that people would try out an activity, enjoy it, and then take it up. These are some examples of past campaigns:

- **Sport for all disabled people (1981).** This campaign coincided with the International Year of the Disabled. Its aims were:
  - to encourage disabled people to take part in physical activities
  - to ensure they had better access to facilities and coaching
  - to encourage the able bodied and disabled to mix in sport
  - to make people more aware of the needs of the disabled.
- **Fifty Plus - All to Play For (1983).** This was aimed at older people. It stressed the importance of exercise and the benefits of physical recreation. Events were organized all over the country, and sports centres arranged special sessions for the over-fifties.
- **Ever Thought of Sport? (1985).** This was aimed at young people (13 to 24), and especially those who had given up sport on leaving school. It was jointly sponsored by Weetabix, with ads on TV and the radio and lots of leaflets.

The Sports Councils

They were set up by Royal Charter. This means they are independent of the government even though it funds them. The monarch must give permission to close them down.

The United Kingdom Sports Council is the most recent one (1996). It deals with overall areas such as doping in sport, sports science, sports medicine, coaching and international sport.

The 'Sport for all disabled people' campaign encouraged archery and many other sports.

Improving facilities

More people taking part in sport and physical recreation means more facilities are needed. The Sports Council helps by:

- giving out grants. Since 1995, most of these come from the National Lottery Sports Fund. (See Unit 14.4.)
- giving advice on designing, building and running facilities.
- designing and testing new kinds of facilities. This includes new kinds of artificial playing surfaces.

Have the campaigns succeeded?

These tables shows results from surveys carried out around the UK. Thousands of people aged 16 and over were asked about their leisure activities. The main physical activities they chose are listed on the right.

% of age group taking part in least one activity from the list							
Year	16 - 19	20 - 24	25 - 29	30 - 44	45 - 59	60 - 69	70 and over
1987	86	77	74	71	56	47	26
1990	87	81	78	73	63	54	31
1993	86	80	77	73	64	51	33

The favourite physical activities
Walking
Swimming
Keep fit/yoga
Cycling
Weight lifting/training
Golf
Running
Football
Badminton
Tennis
Squash
Horse riding
Cricket
Darts
Tenpin bowling/skittles
Fishing
Bowls
Table tennis

Now look at the table above. In 1987, 47% of the group aged 60 - 69 took part in at least one activity. By 1993, six years later, this had risen to 51%. That's an improvement. But it still means that nearly half the group (49%) took part in *none* of the activities.

Into the future

Until 1994, the Sports Councils had a difficult job because there wasn't nearly enough money for facilities. The Lottery Sports Fund has helped to change that. Now an extra £250 million or so is available each year for building and improving facilities.

The government has also realized that the best place to get people interested in sport is in school. So it has special plans for *you*. Find out more in the next Unit.

Questions

1 What were the Sports Councils set up to do?
2 Do you think it is a good idea to have campaigns directed at special groups of people? Why?
3 Do you think the campaign aimed at the disabled had any lasting effects? Give examples.
4 If you had to run a Sports Council campaign, which group would you choose to target? Why?

5 Look at the table above.
a Which of the age groups is most active?
b Had all groups become more active by 1993?
c For which group did participation increase most, between 1987 and 1993?
d Overall, do you think the aim of 'sport for all' has been achieved yet? Explain.

13.5 PE and sport in school

The government has placed great importance on PE and sport in school. What's the difference between them? You take PE during normal lesson time. You play sport *outside* lesson time: it is **extra-curricular**.

Why are PE and sport in school important?

- They help you learn about yourself and your abilities.
- They help to develop teamwork and a sense of fair play.
- They help you develop a fit and healthy body.
- They help you develop self-confidence.
- They give you the chance to enjoy yourself.
- If you get into the habit of regular exercise at school, you are more likely to adopt a healthy lifestyle later.
- They might even lead to a career for you.

PE in the National Curriculum

Everyone from 5 to 16 *must* take PE at school as part of the National Curriculum. You are taught from a range of physical activities that include team games, athletics, gymnastics and dance.

You should also get the chance to take part in sport and other physical activities at lunchtime, after school and at weekends. If your school offers at least four hours of extra-curricular sport a week it may qualify for a **Sportsmark** award.

PE as an exam subject

You can do exams in PE and Sports Studies at GCSE, A level, CFS, and as part of GNVQ courses. This means you can enjoy the subject *and* gain a qualification that could help you find a job later.

PE, health and fitness

You study health and fitness in PE classes. But these topics are so important that schools often teach them in other classes too. Many schools hold health awareness days, with talks and workshops on topics such as smoking, alcohol, drug abuse and AIDS.

> *The Sportsmark Award*
>
> This award is given to a school by the government. To qualify the school must:
>
> - offer at least two hours of PE a week in formal lessons.
> - offer at least four hours of sport a week outside formal lessons.
> - encourage staff to take courses and gain qualifications in coaching.
> - give students the chance to take part in sports competitions in school and against other schools.
> - create links with local clubs to give students more opportunities for sport outside school.
> - encourage students to take part in the award schemes run by governing bodies.
>
> Does your school deserve one?

Some schools are able to offer a wide range of physical activities, both indoors and outdoors.

What physical activities can a school offer?

It depends on:

- the expertise available. A school can't offer an activity if there is no-one to teach it.
- the attitude of the teachers. Many teachers give up free time at lunchtime, after school and at weekends to run sports and other extra-curricular activities. If a teacher is really keen on an activity, it makes a big difference to the school.
  But teachers now have less free time to give, because the National Curriculum has led to an increase in their workload.
- the facilities available. Schools don't always have the money or space for good facilities. Lack of playing fields can be a big problem, especially in city schools.

A school can get round a shortage of expertise and facilities by:

- using the local sports centre. This usually happens for swimming.
- sending students off on courses for activities such as sailing and climbing.
- linking up with a local sports club, so that it can take advantage of its coaching and facilities.

The benefits of links with local clubs

- You may get the chance to play a sport for which your school does not have facilities.
- You get the chance to play more sport outside school hours.
- Clubs can provide qualified coaching so that you reach a higher standard in your sport. Some local clubs send their coaches into schools to help.
- When you know how a club works, you'll find it easier to join one after you leave school. Some clubs encourage school leavers by charging them less to join.

Governing bodies and school sport

The **governing bodies** of sport are the bodies that control and direct it. For example the Amateur Swimming Association and the Football Association. Many of these employ **sports development officers** whose job is to create links with schools and get young people interested in the sport.

Many governing bodies also run award systems for young people, to encourage them in a sport. You can find out more about the governing bodies on pages 163 and 166.

> *The Sports Council*
>
> In line with government policy, the Sports Council is making school sports a priority. For example:
>
> - It gives grants for teachers to go on coaching courses.
> - It gives grants for projects which link schools and local clubs.
> - It helps to arrange sponsorship for school sports by local businesses. For example a business can adopt a school team.
> - It gives grants from the Lottery Sports Fund for school sports facilities, provided there is a shortage of facilities in the area and the local community will be able to use them.

Questions

1 Write down three reasons why sport in school is a good idea.
2 Now try to think of a reason why it's a bad idea.
3 Some people think PE should not be offered as an exam subject. Do you agree with this? Why?
4 Suggest ways a school can make up for a shortage of:
   a coaches for a sport **b** sports facilities.
   Come up with as many ideas as you can.
5 List three things the Sports Council is doing to encourage sport in school.

155

13.6 Towards excellence

The government and Sports Councils are also giving priority to developing top class athletes - the champions.

What you need to be a champion

You need talent and hard work. But you also need:

- top coaching
- top facilities
- financial help
- help from sports science and sports medicine.

The Sports Councils and other bodies are working to improve support for athletes in all these areas.

The National Coaching Foundation (NCF)

This was set up by the Sports Council in 1983 to improve coaching skills. It includes:

- the **Coach Development Unit**. This runs courses for coaches at all levels from beginner to advanced.
- 16 **National Coaching Centres**. These are based in universities and colleges around the UK. They run courses on behalf of the governing bodies and other organizations.
- **Champion Coaching**. This is a scheme for after-school coaching. It is aimed at children aged 11-14 who show promise. The children are put forward by their PE teachers.

Centres of excellence

The United Kingdom has six **centres of excellence** for selected sports. They are funded and run by the Sports Council.

1 **Crystal Palace** in London caters for a range of sports including athletics, swimming, boxing, martial arts and judo. It is also a national and international venue.
2 **Bisham Abbey** in Buckinghamshire is a centre of excellence for tennis. It also caters for football, hockey, squash, weight training and golf.
3 **Lilleshall** in Shropshire is a centre of excellence for football. It also caters for table tennis, cricket, gymnastics, archery, hockey and other sports, and has a sports injuries clinic.
4 **Holme Pierrepoint** near Nottingham is a watersports centre. It has a 2000m regatta lake, ski tow ropes and a canoe slalom.
5 **Plas-Y-Brenin** in Snowdonia in Wales is for mountain and other outdoor activities, including climbing, canoeing, orienteering and dry slope skiing.
6 The **National Cycling Centre** in Manchester. Opened in 1994, it is the newest of the centres.

These centres provide top facilities, coaching and accommodation. They are used mainly by governing bodies to run training programmes and events for their athletes. But they also cater for other users, including beginners.

Athletes preparing in the grounds of Lilleshall.

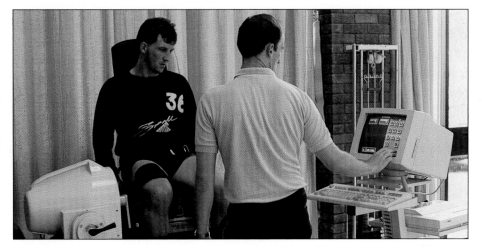

At the centres of excellence, scientific methods are used to help athletes reach their full potential or to recover from injury.

Funding

Training and competing can cost a fortune. The Sports Aid Foundation (page 164) provides grants for some top athletes. Some manage to get sponsorship from business. But many have to work for a living and fund themselves. They often just scrape by. The Sports Council is now working to develop and co-ordinate the sources of funding.

Sports science and sports medicine

For a top athlete, a change in training method, diet or attitude can make all the difference between losing and winning. In the same way one injury can mean the end of the athlete's career. These are the areas where sports science and sports medicine will help.

The United Kingdom Sports Council has overall responsibility for sports science and sports medicine. It funds research in these areas. It also runs a network of sports scientists, who advise the governing bodies and work with top athletes to prepare them for the Olympics and other events.

The National Sports Medicine Institute is a network of experts, from all areas of medicine, with a special interest in sport.

Future plans

In 1995 the government put forward the idea for a **British Academy of Sport**. This would bring together under one roof everything that's needed to help athletes become champions. However, there is debate about whether it should be one big place or several smaller ones in different regions. If the project does go ahead in some shape, it will take several years.

Questions

1 Do you think it's a good idea to develop sports champions? Why?
2 What do the initials NCF stand for?
3 What does the NCF do?
4 Name the UK centre of excellence for:
   a tennis **b** cycling **c** watersports
   d football **e** mountain activities
5 Suppose you were a top weight lifter, with a heavy season of events. List all the things you'd need to spend money on for your sport.
6 Sports scientists include nutrition experts. How might these help athletes perform better?
7 Sports scientists also include psychologists. How might they help athletes perform better?

13.7 Sport in different countries

All governments are interested in sport for all, and excellence in sport. This is not just because they like a good game of football!

Governments and sport

Why a government may promote sport for all	Why a government may promote excellence
• To cut down the nation's health bill. Regular exercise means better health and less demand for medical care.	• To give the nation something to be proud of. When athletes win Olympic gold nearly everyone in the country feels proud of them.
• To cut crime and vandalism. Sport provides an outlet for energy.	• To raise the nation's status in the outside world. This in turn will help trade and tourism.
• To unite different cultural groups within a nation. Sport is something everyone can share.	• To prove that its political system is better than that of other countries.

Sport in the UK

As you saw in the last three Units, the government in the UK is involved in sport through:

- the school curriculum, where PE is compulsory and you can take exams in it.
- the Sports Council, which works to increase participation and promote excellence, and gives grants to improve facilities.

The government does not itself put much money into sport. Most of the money comes from sponsorship, the Lottery Sports Fund, and sports governing bodies.

Even if you are a very talented athlete in the UK, life can be difficult. A young footballer may be spotted by a talent scout and given an apprenticeship by a club and then a contract. But if you run or swim, you may have to find a coach to help you win events. You may have to take a job to support yourself, which makes it difficult to find time for training and competing. Is it easier in other countries?

> **Money motives?**
>
> A government may also promote sport to make money! As you'll see on page 169, the British government makes much more money from sport than it puts back in.

In American colleges, basketball is a high profile game. Competition is intense for team places.

Sport in the USA

In the USA the state governments also promote sport for everyone. But like the UK, it's not very successful. Less than 50% of Americans take part in regular physical activity.

In American secondary school or **high school**, only about half the students in grades 9 - 12 take PE classes. But the athletic students are keen to get on school teams because it brings a lot of status. Sports events between high schools are a big part of school life. People support their local high schools and pay to get in to matches.

If you are a promising athlete, you may get a grant to go to university or **college**. Around $400 million in grants is offered each year. You need certain minimum grades to win one. But the college really wants you for your sports skill, not your brains. This is because sports competition between colleges is very serious, and can make money for the college. It can sell broadcast rights, use of its logo, tickets at the gate and so on.

Many college athletes are so busy with sport that they don't get much time to study. Some use college as a place to get Olympic-level coaching. Some get selected from college to play for professional teams. Many leave college without graduating.

Sport in the developing world

A third world country will have few sports facilities. It needs to spend its money on areas such as education, health and housing. But excellence in sport will help it gain status in the outside world. So it will concentrate on those sports where it can succeed.

Kenya is a good example. It promotes middle and long distance running. Some of its runners have jobs in the army, for example as PE instructors. Some are farmers. At the Barcelona Olympics in 1992, Kenya won 2 gold, 4 silver and 2 bronze medals in running events. How well did it do in Atlanta in 1996?

Sport in the former Eastern Bloc countries

The Eastern Bloc countries included the Soviet Union and East Germany. These were **communist** states. This means the state owned and controlled almost everything, including factories, transport and sports facilities. So it also controlled sport.

The state strongly promoted sport for everyone. This was partly to keep its workers healthy and productive, and partly to strengthen the communist ethos of comradeship, discipline and teamwork. Factories had sports facilities attached. There was a graded system of exercise for every age group, and many sports festivals.

The state also promoted excellence. Promising young athletes - often as young as 6 - went to 'sports schools' where they got special coaching. The best went to sports boarding schools. Top athletes could put off work while they trained. When they took part in events like the Olympic games they did so for the glory of the state.

These countries abandoned communism in the late 1980s and early 1990s. They are turning into **market economies** like the UK and USA. The Soviet Union split up into its original countries such as Russia and the Ukraine. But these still have a strong sports structure in place.

China and Cuba remain communist. Both promote sport strongly. You can probably guess this from the table on the right.

Like Kenya, Morocco has also produced some great runners - this is Khalid Skah, an Olympic champion. Why might developing countries do rather better at running than at sports like tennis?

Olympic medal wins: Barcelona 1992			
Country	No. of medals		
	G	S	B
1 Unified team (ex-Eastern bloc)	45	38	28
2 USA	37	34	37
3 Germany (East and West together)	33	21	38
4 China	16	22	16
5 Cuba	14	16	11

Questions

1 Explain why 'sport for all' might help to:
   a cut a nation's health bill **b** reduce crime
2 Name two differences between the UK and the USA in terms of sport at school and university.
3 Do you think more competition between schools in the UK would be a good idea? Why?
4 'Sport for all' may be a luxury a developing country can't afford. Explain.
5 In the past, communist states have been very successful at the Olympics. Give reasons why.
6 Make a table like the one above for the Atlanta Olympics in 1996. (You may need to use a library.)

Questions on Chapter 13

1 Is it a leisure activity? Explain why.
 a playing netball at lunchtime at school
 b eating meals at home
 c going to the cinema
 d sleeping at night
 e cycling to school
 f playing cards with your friends

2 a Make a list of all the things you do in a normal week.
 b Divide your list into essential and leisure activities.
 c Divide your leisure activities into physical and non-physical.
 d Work out roughly how much time you spend on each activity in a normal week.
 e Make a pie chart to show the information.

3 This shows the results of surveys carried out in three different years. It shows the percentage of people aged 16 and over who took part in the listed physical activities:

Activity	Men			Women		
	1987	1990	1993	1987	1990	1993
Walking	41	44	45	35	38	37
Snooker/pool/billiards	27	24	21	5	5	5
Darts	14	11	9	4	4	3
Cycling	10	12	14	7	7	7
Swimming						
indoor	10	11	12	11	13	14
outdoor	4	4	4	3	4	3
Running/jogging	8	8	7	3	2	2
Golf	7	9	9	1	2	2
Keep fit/yoga	5	6	6	12	16	17
Badminton	4	4	3	3	3	2
Fishing	4	4	4	0	0	0
Squash	4	4	3	1	1	1
Table tennis	4	3	2	1	1	1
Lawn/carpet bowls	2	3	3	1	1	2
Tennis	2	2	3	1	2	2
Cricket	2	2	2	0	0	0

 a Generally women participated less than men. Why do you think this was? Give as many reasons as you can.
 b Women participated *more* than men in two activities. Which were they? Can you explain why?
 c Some activities seem to be getting *less* popular. Which ones? Can you give a reason?
 d The table shows that no women went fishing. Do you think that was true for all women in the UK? Can you explain the figure?
 e For the surveys, people were asked which activities they had taken part in *at least once* in the previous four weeks. Do you think the table gives a good picture of how active people are? Explain why.

4 Match each item **i - vii** below to a letter **A, B** or **C**. Choose the best match each time.
 A recreation
 B physical recreation
 C sport

 i a canoe trip in the summer holidays
 ii playing cricket for the county
 iii listening to music
 iv rollerblading in the park
 v playing rugby union for Wales
 vi playing chess
 vii netball practice after school

5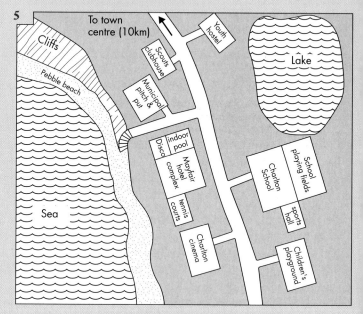

The map above shows part of a coastal town. It is not drawn to scale. This question is about the facilities for physical recreation that appear on the map. Identify:
 a two natural facilities
 b two outdoor built facilities
 c two indoor built facilities
 d one facility provided by private enterprise
 e two provided by voluntary organizations
 f two provided by the local authority

6 Suppose you are a local authority planner. You want to develop the lake in question 5 as a recreational facility.
 a Suggest some activities that could take place there.
 b List all the different groups that might use the lake.
 c Identify any conflicts that might arise between the activities. What steps could you take to avoid them?
 d If you can come up with a project that involves the local community and the school, you might obtain a Lottery Sports Fund grant. Suggest a suitable project.
 e Will you need to build anything round the lake? What? Why?

7 This is a question about your GCSE PE exam. You may need help from your teacher to answer it.

For your GCSE PE exam, you can choose activities from these National Curriculum groups: games, gymnastic activities, dance, athletic activities, outdoor and adventurous activities, and swimming.

  a How many activities can you choose altogether?
  b From how many groups can you choose?
  c Which activities have you chosen for your exam?
  d How will these activities be tested?
  e What percentage of the marks is allocated to them?
  f Do you have to do a written project? If so, what percentage of the marks is allocated to it?
  g What percentage is allocated to the written papers?

8 Some schools offer a wide range of sports. Others offer very few.
  a Name three things that affect how much sport a school can offer.
  b What special problems might schools in inner cities face, with respect to facilities?
  c Explain how a school could offer:
    i tennis, even though it has no tennis courts
    ii climbing, even though it is an inner city school
  d What might prevent the school from doing the things you suggested in **c**?

9 The *Sportsmark Award* is a government award for schools which promote sports strongly. To qualify, the school must meet a number of criteria. It can display the award on its notepaper and prospectuses.
  a List four things a school must do to qualify.
  b Do you think your school would qualify? Explain.

10 For the Sportsmark Award, a school must run competitive sports events within the school, and with other schools.
  a Some people feel competitive sports are very good for you. In what way might they benefit young people?
  b Can you think of any disadvantages of competitive sports for young people?

11 When a country is keen on excellence, it often begins with its children. In China around 30 million young people are at sports school. They are trained using scientific methods.

For example the swimmer Chen Yan started sports school at 6. She joined the national team at 12. In April 1996, aged 15, she beat several Chinese world record holders.

  a List the advantages of early training for young athletes.
  b Now list the disadvantages.
  c Overall, do you think it is a good idea?
  d Find out whether Chen Yan was in China's Olympic team for Atlanta in 1996, and how she performed there.

Things to do

A survey of local facilities
a List the facilities for sport and physical recreation in your area within a radius of 5 km of your school or home. (Yellow Pages or the local Thomson directory will help!)
b For each facility, find out whether it is provided by the local council, private enterprise or a voluntary organization.

A detailed survey of one facility
You may want to work with a partner for this. Choose a local sports or recreational facility. Contact the manager and ask if you can visit the facility as part of a school survey. Find out the answers to these questions.

a What activities does it offer?
b Which different groups of people use it? For example does it welcome disabled people, or mothers with toddlers?
c What provision does it make for the different groups? For example is there a crèche?
d How much does it cost to use? Find out all the different charge rates. For example:
  i Is it less to get in if you become a member?
  ii How much does membership cost?
  iii Are there different rates for the unemployed? families? the over-fifties? retired people? students?
  iv Are there different rates for different times of day?
e Would a person in a wheelchair have any problems in moving around the facility? Walk around and check for ramps, swing doors and so on.
f Does the facility offer social areas such as a café or bar?

Now write a report for the class about the facility.

Sports awards
Many governing bodies of sport offer award schemes to young athletes. Some commercial companies (such as the TSB) run award schemes too.

Find out all you can about award schemes for your sport, and who qualifies for them. Write a report for the class.

Sport in other countries
When athletes win medals in the Olympics, it means they are first class. It also usually means they've had enough support, resources and facilities to help them train and compete.

a Start a tally chart with these headings: Europe, North America, South America, Africa, Asia, Australia.
b Now find a list of the gold medal winners in the Atlanta Olympics. (Try the library?)
c For each winner, put a mark in the correct place in the chart. Which region won most gold medals? Which won least? Can you explain why?
d Find a developing country that won several medals. Were they all for the same sport? Does this surprise you? Why?
e Now find out the top five medal-winning countries in Atlanta. How many are, or were, communist states?

14.1 Organizations (I)

Sport does not develop on its own. It needs hard work and planning. Here and in the next Unit you can find out more about the bodies who control and direct it.

The Sports Council

As you saw on page 152, there are in fact five Sports Councils: the United Kingdom Sports Council, and four separate Councils for England, Scotland, Wales and Northern Ireland.

The job of the United Kingdom Sports Council is:

- to look after those areas affecting UK sport in general. For example coaching, sports science, sports medicine, and doping control.
- to represent the UK on the international scene, and help bring big international sports events to Britain.

For the national Sports Councils, the priorities now are:

- to work with the governing bodies to develop sport at 'grass roots' level, and especially among young people.
- to promote excellence in sport.
- to give out grants from their funds and the Lottery Sports Fund, mainly for building and improving sports facilities.

For more about the work they do, see Units 13.4 - 13.6.

The Sports Council for England...

To make its work more effective, it has divided England into ten regions with an office in each:

Northern, North West,
Yorkshire and Humberside,
Southern, South Western,
Eastern, Greater London, South East,
East Midland, West Midlands.

The Central Council for Physical Recreation (CCPR)

This is an umbrella organization for over 270 governing bodies and associations from all areas of sport and recreation.

To make it easier to manage, they are divided into six groups. Each group elects a committee. These in turn elect the central committee that runs the CCPR. The six groups are:

- games and sports
- major spectator sports
- movement and dance
- outdoor pursuits
- water recreation
- interested organizations.

The aims of the CCPR are:
- to encourage as many people as possible to participate in sport and physical recreation
- to represent and promote the interests of its members.

For money it depends on donations from its members, sponsorship from business, sales of its publications, and a Sports Council grant.

Because it represents so many organizations, the CCPR can tackle issues of general concern. For example the 'unfair' taxation of sport, drug abuse in sport, and sport for the disabled. It provides legal and financial advice for members, and helps them find sponsorship. It also helps to promote British sport abroad.

Some members of the CCPR...

The All England Netball Association

The British Horse Society

The British Judo Association

The British Ski Club for the Disabled

The British Wheel of Yoga

The Cyclists Touring Club

The Football Association

The Guide Association

The Inland Waterways Association

The Keep Fit Association

The National Council for Schools Sports

The Ramblers Association

The Sports Council logo.

The logo for the Central Council for Physical Recreation.

The CCPR shares many of the aims of the Sports Council and works closely with it. But by remaining separate, as a voluntary body, it feels it's in a better position to look after the interests of its members.

National Governing Bodies

Each organized sport has a national **governing body**. Examples are the Football Association and the All England Netball Association.

These bodies are responsible for:

- drawing up the rules of the sport and preventing their abuse
- organizing local and national competitions
- selecting teams for international competitions, for example European and World Championships
- settling disputes within the sport
- managing and coaching referees and umpires
- helping to develop facilities
- maintaining links with similar organizations abroad.

The governing body usually consists of all the regional and county associations, and leagues if they exist. These elect a central council to run it. The county associations in turn represent the local clubs.

The governing body has links with similar governing bodies in other countries, and with the European and World governing bodies. (You can see how this works for swimming on page 166.)

To finance its work, the governing body raises funds from major sporting events, members' subscriptions, sponsorship, grants from the Sports Council and Lottery Sports Fund, and where possible selling broadcast rights for events to radio and TV.

Questions

1 a How many Sports Councils are there?
  b Describe the jobs they do.
2 What does *CCPR* stand for?
3 Describe how the CCPR is organized.

4 Explain how the CCPR helps its members.
5 What does the governing body of a sport do?
6 Name five governing bodies of sport, including the one for your sport.

14.2 Organizations (II)

The Sports Aid Foundation (SAF)

Training and competing in events can cost a lot. Many promising athletes just can't afford it.

The SAF raises money to help these athletes. It does so through sponsorship and donations from business, local authorities, voluntary bodies and the public. Then it gives grants:

- to top athletes, to help them compete with distinction in the Olympic Games and World and European Championships. It concentrates on likely medal winners.
- to promising young athletes and disabled athletes (through SAF Charitable Trust) to help them achieve their full potential.

Athletes must apply through their sport's governing body, which has to approve the application and monitor how the grant is used.

The International Olympic Committee (IOC)

This is the top committee of the Olympic Movement. It is chosen from member countries. Its main jobs are:

- to select the cities where the games will be held
- to decide which sports will be included
- to work with the host city and other bodies to plan the games
- to lead the fight against doping in sport.

For funding, the IOC depends mainly on the sale of TV rights and on sponsorship by multinationals such as Coca Cola and IBM. The American TV company NBC paid around £300 million for the broadcast rights to the Atlanta games. Sponsors are not allowed to advertise in the Olympic stadiums. But they can use the Olympic symbols on their products. They get access to exclusive hospitality at the games, and to the best advertising slots when the games are broadcast.

The money the IOC receives is divided up between the IOC, the International Sports Federations, the National Olympic committees, and the local Organizing Committee for each Olympics.

The British Olympic Association (BOA)

The BOA is part of the Olympic Movement. Its main jobs are:

- to select the British team for the Olympic Games
- to raise money to send the team to the games
- to make all the arrangements for getting it there
- to work with the governing bodies to prepare the athletes.

Although the BOA gets some money from the IOC, it is not nearly enough to support a team. The BOA raises the extra it needs from sponsorship, licensing its logo (for use on mugs and T-shirts for example), and donations from the public.

In keeping with the Olympic ideals the BOA steers clear of politics. In 1980 the government wanted it to boycott the Moscow games in protest at the Soviet invasion of Afghanistan. The BOA refused.

> **Some expenses for a top athlete**
> - coaching fees
> - travel to training facilities, which may sometimes be overseas
> - use of training facilities
> - travel to events, including flights
> - fees to enter events
> - accommodation when away from home
> - food including any special diets
> - equipment
> - sports kit such as footwear
> - insurance
> - medical help such as physiotherapy.

The BOA logo, incorporating the Olympic rings.

The scoreboard at every Olympics carries this message. Do you think athletes, coaches and spectators agree with it?

The Countryside Commission helps to maintain National Trails and other routes for walkers, like this one in Yorkshire.

The Countryside Commission (CC)

The Countryside Commission looks after the English countryside and advises the government on countryside matters. It is funded by the Department of the Environment.

The CC is not directly concerned with sport. But it plays a part in physical recreation. Its aim is to ensure that the countryside is enjoyed but also protected. It is involved in:

- developing and looking after National Trails for walkers, cyclists and riders. These include the Pennine Way and Cleveland Way.
- restoring public rights of way. There are over 190 000 km of paths through the country where you have the right to walk freely.

It also looks after the most beautiful parts of the English countryside:

- the seven National Parks, which include Dartmoor and Exmoor.
- the Heritage Coasts.
- the landscapes protected as Areas of Outstanding Natural Beauty. These include Pennine moorlands and the Surrey Hills.

Scotland and Wales have similar organizations: the Scottish Natural Heritage and the Countryside Council for Wales.

COUNTRYSIDE COMMISSION

The logo of the Countryside Commission.

Questions

1 The SAF helps British athletes achieve excellence.
   a Explain why this is true.
   b Where does it get the money?
2 What is the *IOC*? What are its main jobs?
3 What is the *BOA*? What are its main jobs?

4 Suppose your job is to get the British team to the Olympics and look after it there. List all the things you'd need to consider.
5 Describe two ways the Countryside Commission helps people to enjoy physical recreation.

14.3 Inside a sport

To run local, national and international events, a sport has to be well organized.

The organization of a sport

Let's take swimming as an example. You read about governing bodies on page 163. The governing body for swimming in England is the Amateur Swimming Association (ASA). This shows how the ASA is related to other governing bodies (gb) of swimming, and to the local clubs:

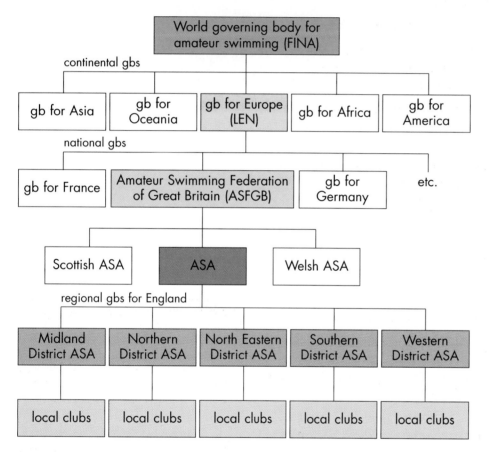

If you are a talented swimmer you start off at the bottom, competing in local events. You win and move up to regional events, then national events, and finally to international competitions.

The local clubs

The job of any local club in any sport is:

- to provide facilities
- to organize competitions
- to promote the sport and encourage new members.

One good way to encourage new members is to make links with local schools. This also benefits schools, as you saw on page 155.

A successful club can act as a focus for the community, and give it a strong sense of pride. Can you think of any big club that does this?

Inside a club

All clubs have much the same structure, no matter what size they are or what the sport is.

Everyone who joins the club is a **member** and has to pay a membership fee. The members elect a **committee** to run the club. The committee members are the club **officials**. The committee meets regularly, for example every fortnight, to make decisions about the club's activities.

The committee

The chair person. This is the top official of the club. He or she represents the club and presides at meetings.

Vice-chair. This person takes over if the chair person is absent.

Secretary. The secretary arranges meetings, keeps **minutes** or written records of the discussions in them, and makes sure everyone is informed about decisions that have been taken.

Treasurer. The treasurer looks after the club's finances and manages its bank account. Cheques paid out must usually be signed by the treasurer and at least one other club official.

Other officials. Depending on its size, a club may have several other officials. For example a fixtures secretary to organize events, a membership secretary to find and enroll new members, and a coach.

Where the club gets its funding

Local clubs usually get their funding from:

- membership fees and match fees. For example in a squash club you have to pay a fee when you book a court.
- grants from the local authority or the sport governing body.
- sponsorship from local companies.
- fundraising events such as barbecues and raffles.

Big **professional** clubs such as Manchester United can raise large sums of money from ticket sales and from selling **merchandise** such as strip, flags and posters. Look at the box on the right.

Some large clubs are **public limited companies** or **plcs**. This means they have shareholders who put money into the company by buying shares in it, and expect a share of the profits in return. Manchester United is one example.

Manchester United's earnings, 1995	
	£ million
Gate receipts and programme sales	19.6
Television	6.8
Sponsorship, royalties and advertising	7.4
Conference and catering	3.4
Merchandising and other	23.4
Total	60.6

Questions

1 For your sport, what is the name of:
  a the World governing body?
  b the European governing body?
  c the UK governing body?

2 Name three different officials you'd find in any sports club, and say what their jobs are.

3 See if you can find the name of another football club that's a public limited company.

14.4 Finance in sport

It costs a lot to build and run sports facilities, organize events, buy equipment and train athletes. Who pays?

Where does the money come from?

National government. The government raises money each year from taxes and other sources. Then at Budget time the Chancellor decides how much can be spent, and divides it among the different government departments.

The Department of National Heritage is responsible for sport. It decides how much of its share will go to sport. Most of this (around £47 million a year) is divided among the five **Sports Councils**. They use the money to help develop sport, improve facilities and promote excellence. You can find out more about them in Units 13.4 - 13.6 and 14.1.

Local government. Your local council raises money by means of the **council tax** which each household pays, and the **business tax** paid by shops and other businesses. It uses the money to build and maintain schools and recreational facilities as well as for services such as the police, fire brigade and refuse disposal.

The governing bodies of sport. They earn money from things like:

- selling permission for events to be broadcast on TV and radio. For example the Football Association made a TV deal worth £250 million in 1995.
- selling tickets for major events such as cup finals and Wimbledon.

They then plough most of the money back into their sports.

The National Lottery. This was launched in 1994. Every week we buy around 70 million lottery tickets and 20 million scratch cards.
For each £1 spent on a lottery ticket 5.6p goes to the Lottery Sports Fund. (It's almost the same for a scratch card.) The fund is handled by the Sports Councils who award it as grants for sports projects.

Sponsorship. This is a big source of finance for sport. For example:

- Rover sponsors the tennis school at Bisham Abbey.
- Bass the brewers sponsor Premier League football matches.

But sponsorship isn't just for big projects and big names. A local business might pay for a trophy or the strip for the local junior football team. There is more about sponsorship in Unit 15.2.

Private individuals. A wealthy person may donate a large sum to a favourite club, or even buy it! Jack Walker, a millionaire from the steel industry, is owner and chairman of Blackburn Rovers. Alan Sugar of Amstrad is owner and chairman of Tottenham Hotspur.

Sales of tickets and merchandise. Clubs get money by selling tickets to events, and things like sweat shirts, scarves, flags and posters. You saw on page 167 how much Manchester United can make from these sources.

Membership fees. Small clubs like the local squash club charge a membership fee to cover running expenses.

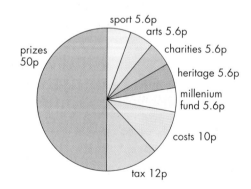

A National Lottery Ticket: where the £1 goes

prizes 50p
sport 5.6p
arts 5.6p
charities 5.6p
heritage 5.6p
millenium fund 5.6p
costs 10p
tax 12p

Grand National Day: a good day for the government! A percentage of the money bet on horses also goes to the Racing Board to help develop the sport.

More about taxation

These are the kinds of taxes we pay the government:

- **a tax on earnings.** Individual earners pay **income tax**. Businesses pay **corporation tax**. The more you earn the more you pay. Even bodies like the Lawn Tennis Association and Football Association have to pay tax.
- **a tax on spending.** A tax called **value added tax** (VAT) is included in the price of most things you buy. For example in the price of CDs, computer games and tickets to football matches.
- **a tax on gambling.** Of each £1 a person bets on the Grand National or other event, the government takes just over 6p. For a £1 lottery ticket (which is also gambling!) the government takes 12p.

Each year the Treasury takes in around £3.6 billion from the taxation of sport. It gives nowhere near that much back to sport.

The Lottery Sports Fund

Suppose a youth club wants to build a new club house. It can apply to the Lottery Sports Fund for a grant. The application goes to a panel which says yes or no. A project will receive funding only if:

- it will benefit the community, including disabled people.
- it involves building or improving something or buying equipment.
- it is well thought out and likely to succeed.
- at least 35% of the total cost will be raised elsewhere (or 10% if you live in a priority area).

The projects can be large or small. In 1996 Welsh Rugby Union was awarded £46 million to build a new stadium and complex in Cardiff. At the same time a sub-aqua club got £2000 to buy equipment.

Who can apply for a Lottery Sports Fund grant?

Organizations like these:

- sports clubs
- youth clubs
- community associations
- sports associations
- governing bodies of sport
- local authorities
- schools and colleges (for facilities they intend to share with the public)

Questions

1 Explain how sport is funded by:
  a national government b local government
2 When a person spends £1 on a lottery ticket, where does the money go?
3 Describe three taxes levied by the government.

4 Which body looks after the Lottery Sports Fund?
5 Think up a sports project for a local youth club which could qualify for lottery funding. How will it benefit the local community, including disabled people? Describe it as fully as you can.

14.5 International sport

Sport brings people of all races together, regardless of their differences.

The benefits of international sport

- It gives players and supporters from different countries the chance to meet and develop friendship.
- It unites people from different races, religions, cultures and classes in a shared interest.
- It gives the world's top athletes the chance to compete against each other. This encourages excellence.
- It spreads interest in sport and encourages more people to play.

International events

Most sports hold international events arranged by their international governing bodies. For example European and World Cup football tournaments are arranged by UEFA (the European governing body) and FIFA (the World governing body). Who do you think would organize the European and World Swimming Championships? (Check the diagram on page 166.)

Events such as the Commonwealth Games and the Olympics cover a wide range of sports. They are arranged by separate organizations with help from the governing bodies. For example the International Olympics Committee (page 164) arranges the Olympics and Winter Olympics, which now include 33 sports altogether.

Hosting international events

The **host** is the city or country staging the events. The **venue** is the stadium where an event is held.

The Olympics are hosted by cities - for example Sydney in 2000. But many events are hosted by countries and spread around several centres. England was the host for Euro'96, the 1996 European Nations Football Championships. The venues were in Birmingham, Leeds, Liverpool, London, Manchester, Newcastle, Nottingham and Sheffield.

Some advantages of playing host

Countries and cities often compete fiercely for the chance to host an international sports event. Why?

- For prestige. It is considered an honour to host the Olympics. If the event is a success, the host city gains prestige. This can pay off in all kinds of ways, including an increase in trade and tourism.
- It unites the country and gives a sense of pride.
- It gives a boost to sports facilities – and other facilities. Cities build or improve their facilities to host events. The local people can enjoy these long after the events are over.
- The event may make a profit. Sales of radio and TV rights, tickets and merchandise can bring in a lot of money. Local shops, restaurants, hotels, taxis and other services will also benefit.

The Olympic ideals

The aim of the Olympics is to promote:

- personal excellence
- sport as education
- cultural exchange
- mass participation
- fair play
- international understanding

The opening ceremony at the Seoul Olympics in 1988. Countries line up years in advance to compete for the chance to host the Olympics.

Some disadvantages of playing host

- If it runs into problems in organizing an event, the country or city may lose money. Montreal made a loss of over $1 billion with the Olympic Games in 1976. The debt will take years to pay off.
- An event that attracts hooligans puts a big strain on the police. They may have to patrol trains and airports as well as venues.
- A large number of visitors means extra strain on hotels, transport, water supplies and so on. If these can't cope there will be problems.
- Big events are security risks. They are watched on TV by millions of people, so terrorists and other groups may use them to air their grievances. They may be disrupted by bomb threats, strikes and riots.
- If an event does not go well the host's image suffers. The host will have difficulty attracting other events.

International sport and politics

Sport *can* promote peace and understanding. But where countries are already enemies, they may use sport as a form of 'cold war'.

- A country may decide to boycott an event for political reasons.
- It may use its top athletes to prove it is more powerful than its enemy, or that its political system is superior.

The Olympic Games are the world's biggest and most spectacular sports event. Over the years they have often been used for political purposes. You can find out more about this in the next Unit.

International sport and money

It can be wildly expensive to stage an international event. This means:

- poor countries just can't afford them.
- even the rich countries can't afford major events without sponsorship and the sale of broadcast rights. For example it cost around $1.7 billion to stage the Atlanta Olympics (over £1 billion).

Some people think that the Olympics are now *too* commercial, with entertainment and profit as important as sport. What do you think?

The Atlanta Games 1996

- 26 sports
- 271 events
- Over 10 000 athletes
- Cost: around $1.7 billion
- Profit: around $13 million

Questions

1 Write down two benefits of international sport.
2 Name a city that has hosted:
   a the Summer Olympics b the Winter Olympics
   c the Commonwealth Games
3 Your city plans to host an international football event. List all the things it will need to consider.

4 a Write down two advantages of hosting an international sports event.
   b Now write down two disadvantages.
5 Do you agree that the Olympic Games encourage:
   a excellence? b mass participation in sport?
   Explain why.

14.6 Trouble at the Games!

The Olympics are the world's biggest and most famous sports event. This means they are also open to big political and financial problems, as you will see below.

1936 Berlin
The games were awarded to Berlin in 1931. By 1936 Hitler and the Nazis had risen to power, but it was too late to move the games.

Hitler used the games to show off Nazi power and to try to prove his theory that the world's blonde, blue-eyed, Northern races (the Aryan races) were superior. On the first day the German Hans Woellke won gold in the shot putt. Hitler paraded him as an Aryan champion.

But the black American athlete Jesse Owens was the star of the Games, winning four gold medals. When the crowd rose to salute Owens, Hitler left the stadium.

1956 Melbourne
Just weeks before these games, Britain and France invaded Egypt in a conflict over the Suez Canal. Egypt, Iran and Lebanon withdrew from the games in protest.

China also withdrew because Taiwan ('free China') had entered a team. Spain, Holland and Switzerland withdrew because the Soviet Union had invaded Hungary. A semi-final in water polo between Hungary and the Soviet Union was abandoned because a vicious fight broke out between the teams.

1968 Mexico City
Before the games, the homeless were cleared from Mexico City so that visitors would not see them. Mexican students protested about this and the money spent on the games. While people everywhere watched on TV, over 300 rioting students were shot dead by soldiers.

Among the winners at these games were the black American sprinters Tommie Smith and John Carlos. During their medal ceremony they stood with heads bowed and clenched fists raised in a black power salute. They were expelled by the US Olympic Association and sent home immediately.

These games are remembered by high jumpers for another reason. The American Dick Fosbury showed off his winning technique and the Fosbury Flop was born.

1972 Munich
During these games, Palestinian terrorists broke into the Olympic village. They took nine Israeli team members hostage and killed two others. In return for the hostages they demanded the release of 200 Palestinians held in Israeli prisons.

The German police attempted a rescue. It failed, and the nine athletes were killed along with a policeman and five terrorists. After this tragedy, many officials and atheletes wanted the Munich games to be abandoned. But the IOC decided they should carry on.

Jesse Owens, star of the 1936 Olympics – to Hitler's chagrin.

1976 Montreal

The Canadian government made lavish plans for the games. But after industrial disputes and a long hard winter, the money ran out. The opening ceremony took place in an unfinished Olympic stadium, and the athletes had poor accommodation. Montreal is still paying off its $1 billion Olympic debts.

The games also suffered a boycott by African countries. They were objecting to New Zealand's rugby links with apartheid South Africa. Twenty-two black African teams flew home when the IOC refused to ban New Zealand.

1980 Moscow

The Soviet Union invaded Afghanistan in December 1979. In protest, West Germany, Kenya, Japan, Canada and America boycotted the Moscow games.

1984 Los Angeles

These games marked the start of a new era: they were the first to be completely funded by sponsorship and the sale of broadcast rights. They made a profit of $215 million. (Since 1984, no games have made anywhere near this.) But critics felt they had become a commercial show and that athletes were being used to generate profit.

The games were boycotted by the Soviet Union and many of its allies. The reason they gave was the poor security arrangements. The real reason was to pay America back for boycotting Moscow in 1980.

1988 Seoul

Seoul is in South Korea. North Korea, which is a communist country, wanted to stage some of the events. But the IOC refused. In protest, North Korea and four of its allies boycotted the games.

These games also marked the return of tennis, with professional players. It had been banned in 1924 because of doubts about the amateur status of tennis players. But in 1981 the rule about amateur status had been dropped. (You can find out more about this in Unit 15.1.)

1992 Barcelona

These were successful games. No-one boycotted them. They continued the trend towards commercialisation. They made a small profit.

South Africa sent a team for the first time in over 30 years. (It had been expelled in the early 1960s for its apartheid policy.) East and West Germany combined to form a single team for the first time since 1964.

Back in business - the South African team in 1992.

The Modern Olympic Games	
1886	Athens
1900	Paris
1904	St Louis
1908	London
1912	Stockholm
1916	Cancelled due to World War I
1920	Antwerp
1924	Paris
1928	Amsterdam
1932	Los Angeles
1936	Berlin
1940	Cancelled due to World War II
1944	Cancelled due to World War II
1948	London
1952	Helsinki
1956	Melbourne
1960	Rome
1964	Tokyo
1968	Mexico City
1972	Munich
1976	Montreal
1980	Moscow
1984	Los Angeles
1988	Seoul
1992	Barcelona
1996	Atlanta
2000	Sydney
2004	?

Questions

1 Give one example of Olympic Games where:
   a politics led to violence
   b the financing of the games caused problems.

2 Find out more about the conflict that led to China's boycott of the games in 1956. (Try the library.)

3 a South Africa was banned from the Olympics for many years. Why was this?
   b When was it welcomed back, and why?

4 East and West Germany had one team between them at Barcelona. What made this possible?

Questions on Chapter 14

1 What do the initials stand for?
   i CC
   ii IOC
   iii BOA
   iv CCPR

2 True or false?
   A The Queen is in charge of the Sports Council.
   B There are three Sports Council bodies.
   C The CCPR is in charge of all leisure centres.
   D The BOA is controlled by the government.
   E The IOC leads the fight against drug abuse in sport.
   F The IOC is a non-profit-making organization.
   G The CC promotes physical recreation.

3 To answer this question you may need to look back at Units 13.4 - 13.6 as well as Unit 14.1.
   a Why were the Sports Councils first set up?
   b How many are there now, and what are they called?
   c Name two past Sports Council campaigns that were aimed at particular target groups. What was the purpose of these campaigns?
   d Name three things the Sports Councils do to promote excellence.
   e Name three things the Sports Councils do to increase the number and quality of sports facilities.
   f Name two things the Sports Councils do to promote sport among young people at school.
   g Since 1994 the Sports Councils have been able to give out more grants for sports facilities. Why?
   h What kind of work does the UK Sports Council do?

4 One thing the Sports Councils have done is to create standard plans for sports centres. The scheme is called Standard Approach to Sports Halls (SASH). Local authorities all over the country can use these plans to build sports centres that look very similar.
   a In what ways is this a good idea? Think of as many as you can.
   b Can you think of any way in which it's a bad idea?

5 The bodies that control sport often have well-known people on their committees. See if you can name one well-known person who is an official in:
   a the Sports Council for England
   b the United Kingdom Sports Council
   c the British Olympic Association.

6 This question is about the Central Council for Physical Recreation (CCPR).
   a It is an umbrella organization. What does that mean?
   b Name five organizations that belong to the CCPR.
   c Give two reasons why the CCPR is a useful body.

7 The Football Association (FA) is the governing body for football in England.
   a Name the World governing body for football.
   b Name the European governing body.
   c List four functions of the FA.

8 This shows how much the local tennis club expects to spend in the coming year:

	£
Redecoration of the club house	1800
Repairs to courts	800
New nets	1700
Coaching fees	800
Groundsman	1000
Insurance	550
Post and phone	450
	7100

   a The club has 70 members. It charges £30 a year for membership. How much money does that bring in?
   b It costs £1 to book a court. Last year there were 1000 bookings. How much did that bring in?
   c Suppose the bookings remain at the same level next year. How much more money will the club need to find, to cover its costs for the year?
   d You are the club treasurer. You are determined that the club will not make a loss next year. Write a list of suggestions for ways to raise money, which you will present at the next committee meeting.

9 Every week around £90 million is spent in the UK on National Lottery tickets and scratch cards. This list shows where each £1 from a lottery ticket goes. You can assume that the money from scratch cards is divided in the same way. (It is very similar.)

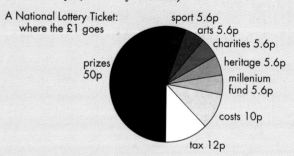

A National Lottery Ticket: where the £1 goes — prizes 50p, sport 5.6p, arts 5.6p, charities 5.6p, heritage 5.6p, millenium fund 5.6p, costs 10p, tax 12p

   a How much from each £1 goes on sport?
   b About how much does sport gain altogether each week?
   c About how much goes to the government each week?
   d Where does most of the money go?
   e Write a paragraph in favour of the National Lottery, showing how it benefits society. Give examples.
   f Now write a paragraph describing its harmful effects.
   g Overall, are you in favour of the Lottery or against it?

10 a Even though you don't earn, you still pay tax now and then, for example when you buy a CD. Explain this.

b Working people pay a tax that depends on the size of their income. What is it called?

c Households also pay a tax.
   i   What is this tax called?   **ii** Who collects it?
   iii Name three things the money is used for.

d Give four examples of how the government makes money from sport.

11 Copy and complete this table about past Olympics.

Date	Host city	Issue
1936	Berlin	Games used as Nazi propaganda
	Melbourne	
	Mexico City	
	Munich	
1976		
1980		
	Los Angeles	
1988		
	Barcelona	

12 These are some of the jobs carried out in Atlanta to prepare for the 1996 Olympics:
 – new sports venues built and others updated
 – aging bridges, streets and sewers overhauled
 – the airport renovated
 – detailed plans made for safety and security
 – over $1.7 billion (£1.1 billion) raised to cover the costs
 – over 11 million tickets distributed round the world.

a List all the different kinds of people needed for these jobs. Include architects and engineers, for example.

b How did the games benefit Atlanta's citizens? Think of as many ways as you can.

c What problems, if any, arose during the games? (Check this out in a library if you need to.)

d Do you think the games were a success? Explain.

13 The Atlanta Games made only a very small profit. Future Olympics are expected to do the same. One reason is the high cost of security. Another is that the world expects a more dazzling display each time.

a Give reasons why security is a big concern.

b Do you think display and pageantry are necessary for the games? Explain your answer.

c In spite of small profits, countries are already lining up to host the games for 2008. Why should they want to do this?

14 Critics of the Olympics have suggested these changes:
 • no national uniforms for athletes
 • no national anthems or flags during medal ceremonies.

a What positive effects might these changes have?

b Can you think of any negative effects they'd have?

Things to do

Sports bodies

These organizations were described in the last two chapters:
 • The Sports Council
 • The National Coaching Foundation (NCF)
 • The Central Committee for Physical Recreation (CCPR)
 • The six centres of excellence
 • The Sports Aid Foundation (SAF)
 • The Countryside Commission (CC)
 • The British Olympic Association (BOA)
 • The International Olympic Association (IOC)
 • The National Lottery and its Sports Fund.

Select one student for each organization. He or she should write to the organization and ask for more information about it.

National governing bodies

Choose five sports played by people in your class. Five students should take one sport each, and write to that sport's governing body for more information. Find out:

a what the governing body does

b how the sport is structured

c how the governing body raises finance

d what it does to promote its sport in schools.

Finance and sport in your school

Is your school in need of some new sports equipment, or repairs to sports facilities? Draw up a list of what needs doing. Then the class should choose just one item for which to raise money. (Don't be too ambitious. Choose something realistic.)

a Describe what is needed and find out roughly what it would cost. You may need help from your teacher for this.

b Now have a brainstorming session in class about how to raise the money. In brainstorming, everyone calls out an idea in turn, without worrying about whether it is stupid. One person writes the ideas on the board as they are called out. Allow say 12 minutes for this activity.

c Now go through the list and pick out the 4 or 5 best ideas. Decide how much money you could raise from each one.

d Write a project proposal from the class to your head teacher, explaining what you want to do and why, and setting out your plans very clearly. Request permission to go ahead with the project.

International sports events

1 a Use a library to find out about the history of the Olympic Games. Your research should include: the ancient Olympic Games and why they were held; the Frenchman who started the modern Olympics; the participation of women in the modern Olympics; the start of the Winter Olympics.

b Write a short essay on the history of the games. It should be no more than two pages.

2 Now find out when and why the Commonwealth Games were started. Write about half a page on their history.

15.1 Amateur or professional?

How do you tell who's amateur and who's not?

- **Amateurs** do not get paid for playing their sport. The theory is they do it for love of the sport.
- **Professionals** play full time and get paid for it. It's how they earn their living.
- **Semi-professionals** are like professionals but play only part time and have another job too.

The term *amateur* was originally a sign of social class. It meant you were a gentleman who could afford to play a sport just for pleasure. There's more about this on page 189.

Who decides?

The rules about amateurs and professionals, and what they can and can't do, are made by a sport's international governing body.

- Many sports divide players clearly into professionals and amateurs, with the professionals at the top. Football is an example. Amateurs and professionals don't usually compete together, except in specific events. For example amateur and professional golfers can compete in an 'open' golf tournament.
- In some sports most athletes, even the top ones, are 'amateur'. Swimming and athletics are examples. The athletes can't accept money for playing their sports. But see below for ways around this!
- Some sports are **open**. Amateurs and professionals can compete freely in most events. Horse racing and tennis are examples.

Are top amateurs really not paid?

To be a top athlete you need to devote yourself full time to your sport. But if you're not allowed to earn money from it, how do you survive?

Scholarships. In America young athletes get scholarships to colleges with a good reputation for their chosen sport. Scholarships can cover everything: food, board, books and tuition. The athletes train with top coaches in top facilities. They don't have to worry about money.

The same thing is also beginning to happen here. Several UK universities now offer sports scholarships.

'Jobs'. In many countries athletes are given token 'jobs', for example as PE instructors in the army or police force, so that they can train full time. This often happens in developing countries.

Special training camps. Promising young athletes may be sent to sports schools and then training camps, where they remain long past the age when most people get a job. This is usual in China.

Trust funds. Since 1983, athletes in athletics can accept prize and appearance money. But not directly. It is paid into a **trust fund** in order to preserve their amateur status. Money from the fund is used to cover the athlete's training and living expenses. He or she gets the rest on retirement. (Rugby Union also used this system until 1995.)

Some football teams

Professional
Newcastle United
Tottenham Hotspur
and similar league teams

Semi-professional
Woking
Kidderminster Harriers
and similar non-league teams

Amateur
Your local Sunday team

Some open sports
angling
bowling
cricket
mountaineering
squash
tennis

Grants and sponsorships. Amateur athletes can seek grants from the Sports Aid Foundation (page 164) for example, or sponsorship from business. The governing bodies must approve these.

Why keep the distinction?

As you can see, top 'amateur' athletes get 'paid' indirectly in all kinds of ways. So the distinction between amateurs and professionals is a fuzzy one. Why not just drop it and make all sports open?

The fear is that money would then become the main reason for competing, with athletes aiming to win at all costs and by any methods. The ideal of fair play might go out the window. Governing bodies might lose control of their sports to commercial organizations.

Amateurism and the Olympic Games

The Olympic Games were meant for amateurs. Tennis was dropped in the 1920s because of doubts about the players' status.

But over the years it has been obvious that many competitors are not truly amateur, and many winners are rewarded when they get home, for example with cars, jobs and houses. In 1981 the term 'Olympic amateur' was dropped from the rules. Tennis, with professional players, was allowed back in 1988. But the only prizes offered at the Olympics are the Olympic medals.

The final decision about who can take part in the games is now left to the International Sports Federations. Some sports uphold the amateur ideal more strictly than others. For example professional footballers can now take part in the games but professional boxers cannot.

The story of Rugby League and Rugby Union

Rugby began at Rugby School. The rules were laid down in 1846. By 1881 Rugby Union governing bodies had been set up in England, Scotland and Wales.

But in 1895 Rugby League was born when 22 northern clubs broke away. Their players wanted compensation for the time spent away from work training and playing. Rugby Union had refused them.

Rugby League became the professional game, and developed its own rules over the years. Then in 1995, a hundred years later, Rugby Union finally backed down and let professional players in.

Linford Christie, the great 100m runner. Technically an 'amateur', this top athlete has earned a great deal from sport and related activities.

St Helens lift Rugby League's Challenge Cup, 1996.

Questions

1 What is an *amateur* athlete? Name one top athlete who has amateur status.
2 What is a *professional* athlete? Name four.
3 What is an *open* sport? Name four.
4 To remain 'amateur', athletes must not earn a living from their sport. Describe three ways round this.
5 Are the Olympic Games still strictly for amateurs?
6 When and why did Rugby League form?

15.2 Sponsorship

Without a sponsor, many athletes couldn't carry on with their sport.

What is sponsorship?

Sponsorship is where a business provides support (usually financial) for an event or team or athlete. Watch sport on TV and you'll see sponsors' brand names on players' clothing and hoardings around the venues.

Why sponsor sport?

It is a way to advertise. The sponsor's name is displayed before the spectators all through the event.

Advantages to the sponsor

- Sport has a healthy, positive image. Businesses like to be associated with this.
- Sponsorship is often **tax-deductible**. This means the business does not have to pay tax on the amount it spends on sponsorship. (That is one way the government helps to promote sport.)
- TV sports events are seen in millions of homes. So is the sponsor's brand name. An event like Wimbledon or a Cup Final reaches millions of TV screens round the world. This means a sponsor's logo reaches places that may be very difficult or expensive to reach with other kinds of advertising.
- When a local business sponsors a local team, it gains the good will of the local people.
- In exchange for sponsorship a sponsor may get the best seats at an event, or the use of luxury executive boxes. The sponsor can use these to entertain clients.

Disadvantages to the sponsor

- The sponsor expects the athlete or team to behave well, or the event to go smoothly. This cannot be guaranteed. If an event is disrupted by hooliganism or the weather, or an athlete is caught doping or cheating, or gets involved in a scandal, the sponsor won't be happy.
- The sponsor also hopes the team or athlete will be successful. That can't be guaranteed either.

Forms of sponsorship

Sponsorship may be for:

- a sport. Budweiser sponsors American football in the UK.
- a single event. Flora sponsored the 1996 London Marathon.
- a team. Sharp sponsors Manchester United. So do several other companies, as you'll see if you check out the players' kit.
- an individual. Linford Christie has been sponsored by Lucozade and Toyota, among others.

Sponsorship is not always money. A car manufacturer may provide free transport, and an airline free flights. A company that makes sports goods may provide clothing and equipment. A food company may provide food. Sponsorship for a young person could be in the form of a scholarship to a centre of excellence.

The 1996 London Marathon, sponsored mainly by Flora. You can usually tell from the size of the banners which company has provided most sponsorship.

> *Sponsorship in schools*
>
> The Sports Council encourages business to sponsor sports in school. For example to sponsor:
>
> - a school team
> - a school pitch
> - coaching by outside coaches
> - school transport to sports events
> - inter-school competitions
> - scholarships to centres of excellence.

Finding sponsorship

It can be hard for an unknown young athlete to find sponsorship. Sponsors like a safe bet! Athletes, coaches and agents spend a lot of time calling on companies and very often the answer is no.

A sport may have difficulty finding sponsorship if it doesn't have a slot on TV. Big sponsors like high profile TV sports. Far more people watch sports on TV than at live venues.

It can be specially difficult for female or black athletes. Sponsors who make computers and upmarket cars aim their ads at the spectators with most spending power. These tend to be youngish, white and male. The sponsors go for the favourite sports, events and stars of this group.

But if you're a sports star you'll have no problem getting sponsorship. Companies will queue up to pay you to **endorse** their products: to wear their clothing, drink their soft drinks or drive their cars. Top athletes can earn more from these deals than from their sport.

The benefits and drawbacks for sport

Benefits for sport

- To promote and develop a sport you need to stage events. This can be very expensive. Sponsorship makes it possible.
- Sponsorship also helps talented athletes to train and compete when they couldn't otherwise afford to.
- For top athletes, it can be very lucrative. This is useful because their careers may be short.

Drawbacks for sport

- A deal lasts only a certain time. It does not give a team or an athlete long-term security.
- A sponsor may be bad for a sport's image. Sponsorship by alcohol and tobacco companies is not allowed for events for the under-18s. There is also pressure on TV companies to stop broadcasting events that are sponsored by tobacco companies.
- Sponsors may want to dictate the timing of sports events to suit their own purposes. For example to coincide with peak viewing time on TV. This might not be best for the athletes.
- Teams and athletes may feel exploited by sponsors. This can lower their satisfaction with sport and their motivation to succeed.

Sports stars like Andre Agassi can earn thousands just by taking a sip from a sponsor's soft drink during a match. Wearing a sponsor's clothing or sports shoes earn him a whole lot more.

Questions

1 What is *sponsorship*?
2 Describe two benefits to the sponsor.
3 Now describe two possible problems for the sponsor.
4 Give two other real-life examples (not used here) of sponsorship for: a a team b an individual

5 Female rugby teams have particular difficulty in obtaining sponsorship. Try to explain why.
6 Give one benefit and one drawback of sponsorship for:
   a a team b an individual
7 On balance, is sponsorship a good idea? Why?

179

15.3 Sport and the media

The **media** are all the means by which information is delivered to you: books, newspapers, magazines, radio, TV, cinema and video.

How the media affect sport

The media have an enormous impact on sport. This is particularly true of TV. Some of the effects are good, some not!

Positive effects

- The media help to promote sport. Sporting events are seen, heard and read about by millions of people.
- They create sports 'stars' who may inspire young athletes. Judy Simpson and Eric Cantona are examples.
- When a sport gets a lot of media attention, more people get interested in playing it.
- Sports that get a lot of media coverage, especially on TV, find it easier to obtain sponsorship.
- The media can educate and inform you about sport. For example through documentaries, coaching programmes and discussion of current issues.
- TV companies pay large sums to the governing bodies of sport for the right to broadcast events. This is used to develop the sport.

Dance and other activities also benefit from the media in these ways.

Some drawbacks

- Media exposure may foster the desire to win at all costs rather than play for enjoyment.
- There is more pressure on managers and team captains to get results. The media may hound them out of their jobs if they fail.
- Sports stars lose privacy. Their private lives get reported on.
- TV may force changes on a sport. In 1996 Rugby League changed from being a winter game so that TV viewers could see it all year round. The tie break in tennis was introduced to appeal to a TV audience.
- The media may over-sensationalise events. Why would they do this?

How the media present sport

When you read about something in the paper, or watch it on TV, or listen on the radio, it is *not* like being there yourself. The event has been 'packaged' for you by the people working in the medium. They have decided what to put in, what to leave out, and what point of view to take.

For example in TV sports the camera operators and video editors decide which shots you see and from which angle. The producers decide who should be interviewed. The interviewers decide which questions to ask.

What you see is often *more* exciting than the actual event, thanks to close-up shots, slow-motion replays, interviews and a dramatic commentary. In real life you would not hear a player's thoughts before a match, or see the pain on a manager's face as his team loses.

From demon to hero: media attention focused on Eric Cantona of Manchester United has made him a household name.

The way an event is packaged in the media depends on how much time, space and money is available. But it also depends on whether the media maker is trying to:

* entertain you
* inform you
* educate you
* 'hype' an event
* attract attention (and sales) by being sensational
* please the sponsors, or
* express a particular point of view.

Another object of intense media interest: Will Carling, then captain of the England rugby team, runs on to the pitch for the first time after the announcement that he was separating from his wife.

Newspapers

Newspapers like sport because it helps to sell them. It also helps to attract advertising. Some companies prefer to advertise their products in the sports pages.

The **tabloid press** includes The Daily Mirror, The Sun and the Daily Express. The **quality press** includes the Independent, Times, Guardian and Daily Telegraph. Both cover sports, but there are differences:

The tabloids tend to ...	*The quality press tends to ...*
go for sensational headlines	go for in-depth coverage and comment
take a strong line of approval or disapproval	do more thoughtful analysis
pay little attention to minority sports	give more coverage to minority sports

In the activities on page 189 you'll have a chance to compare them.

Magazines

There are dozens of different sports magazines. Some cover a range of sports and some just one. They have articles about events, athletes and the latest sports equipment. Some carry out tests on different makes of equipment, which is useful when you're deciding what to buy.

Video

Since you can replay video as much as you want, it is a very good medium for learning about golf, keep-fit and so on. Stores that sell video usually have a sports section. Many sports videos are excellent.

Video of your own sports performance is also useful. You can analyze it in detail and talk it over with your coach.

Questions

1. What is meant by *the media*?
2. List three ways in which media coverage helps sport.
3. Describe three drawbacks of media coverage.
4. Several people play a part in selecting and shaping the information you receive in a sports programme. Name three of them.
5. Give one example of a TV sports programme designed mainly to entertain.
6. Name: **a** one tabloid **b** one quality paper
7. Find a newspaper article about sport which:
   a is sensationalist **b** just gives the facts
8. Why is video a useful medium for sports?

15.4 More about sport and TV

Of all the media, TV has the biggest impact on sport – and vice versa!

How sport benefits TV

You saw in the last Unit how TV and other media benefit sport.
Now look at the way sport benefits TV:

- It is often shown at times when TV would otherwise have few viewers, such as Saturday afternoons. Events like Wimbledon and the Olympics are in summer, which is also a quiet time for TV.
- Sports programmes are much simpler to make than drama or documentaries. You just film the event and edit the film.
- Sport attracts sports fans to TV. Many of them might not otherwise bother watching.
- It also attracts advertisers. TV companies can charge more for their advertising slots during big sports events.

TV and the professional athlete

TV has had a big role in the rise of the professional athlete.

Professional athletes get paid for playing sport. Without all the interest and money generated for sport by TV, many sports could not afford to pay them. Tennis and golf could not offer such big cash prizes. Football clubs could not afford such huge transfer fees.

It is an upward spiral. Sport pays well to attract 'star' players. These players attract more spectators, TV viewers and sponsors. This in turn makes more money for sport.

But it is only the *top* players who make a good living from sport. In the USA for example, tennis players below the top 50 find it hard to get by.

Settled in for the afternoon. Lots of people wouldn't bother with TV if it weren't for sport. (But if they watched less TV, would they play more sport?)

Broadcast rights

In order to show a sports event, a TV company must pay for **broadcast rights**. Payment is usually made to the sport's governing body.

If the company buys **exclusive** rights to a live sports event, it means no one else can film it. The company can then sell footage on to other companies. They may buy just a few minutes to show as highlights.

Different kinds of TV companies

- **Terrestrial.** The terrestrial companies include BBC, ITV and Channel Four. They transmit programmes from TV masts to your TV aerial. You have to pay a TV licence.
- **Satellite.** BSkyB is an example. Information is transmitted via satellite to your satellite dish. You have to pay a subscription fee.
- **Cable.** Videotron is an example. The information is carried along cables buried below the street, with a line fed into your home. You have to pay a subscription fee.

With satellite and cable, the number of TV channels is growing rapidly. Several show sport only. In 1996 BSkyB had three sports channels showing around 60 current sports as well as classic past events.

With the arrival of satellite TV there's been a huge increase in the amount of sport available to the viewer – if you're prepared to pay the subscription fee.

By the end of this century there will be *hundreds* more channels, including sports channels, available to satellite and cable subscribers. Do you think this will encourage more viewers? Or put them off? Many people feel that football is already suffering from over-exposure in the media.

Competition between TV companies

With the increase in TV channels, competition for broadcast rights is fierce. The bids are getting even higher. For example in 1994 the BBC agreed to pay Rugby Union £27 million for the rights to the Five Nations Championships for 3 years. A year later BSkyB agreed to pay £40 million *a year* for the rights to Premier League matches for 5 years.

Government intervention

Satellite and cable companies are ready to pay huge sums for exclusive rights to popular events such as Wimbledon and the FA Cup final. This means that people who don't have a satellite dish or cable TV might not see them at all, or at best just the highlights.

Is this fair? Politicians don't think so. The Broadcasting Bill of 1996 sets out the events to which *everyone* with a TV set should have full access. The list will be continually updated.

> *Proposed list of events to which everyone should have full TV access*
>
> Cricket test matches (where England is playing)
>
> The Derby
>
> The FIFA world cup finals
>
> The FA Cup Final
>
> The Grand National
>
> The Olympic Games
>
> The finals week of Wimbledon
>
> The Scottish FA Cup Final (in Scotland)

Pay-per-view

The first ever **pay-per-view** event in the UK was the world heavy-weight title fight in 1996 between Frank Bruno and Mike Tyson. It was shown on Sky. Viewers had to book in advance and pay extra on top of their normal subscription.

By the end of the century many more sports events will be offered on a pay-per-view basis on satellite and cable channels. In 1996 the BBC announced that it too is planning to provide pay-TV channels in some programming areas.

Interactive TV

By the end of the century **interactive TV** will also be more common. It will give you more control over the information you receive.

For example you'll be able to switch camera angles during a sports event, or press a button for more information about the players. You'll be able to look up the rules of the game, or scores in past matches. Do you think this kind of thing will make sport more exciting?

Questions

1 Describe three ways in which sport benefits TV.
2 What does *exclusive rights* mean?
3 Name: a one terrestrial broadcast company
     b one satellite broadcast company.

4 Think of two ways in which it would benefit a satellite TV company to have the exclusive rights to Wimbledon.
5 What does *pay-per-view* mean?

183

15.5 Participation by women

Why do women participate less than men in sport and physical recreation? Is it because they're not interested?

Women and physical recreation

These are some of the reasons for low participation by women.

Past attitudes to women. A hundred years ago women were regarded as fragile creatures. Vigorous physical activity would harm their internal organs and affect their ability to have children. It was also unladylike to look glowing, tousled or sweaty. A woman should look delicate.

These attitudes persisted for decades among both women and men. (But they didn't necessarily apply to servants!)

Lack of time and energy. The traditional roles for women have been as wife, mother and homemaker. This leaves little time or energy for physical recreation. Now many women work outside the home *and* bring up a family. That means even less free time.

Lack of money. Women who don't have a job outside the home often don't have the money to spend on physical recreation.

Lack of access to facilities. The number of facilities is increasing. But if a woman at home does not have the use of a car, getting to a facility (especially with small children in tow) can take enormous effort.

Participation is increasing

Since the early 1970s women's participation has increased, especially in indoor swimming and keep fit/yoga. This is due to:

- the recognition that exercise is good for your health.
- greater economic freedom. More women are earning more and don't have to depend on men for money.
- Sports Council efforts to promote sport for everyone.
- an increase in the number of facilities offering activities that appeal to women. For example aerobics, swimming and badminton.

But participation is still far too low, as you can see from the tables on the right. There is a long way to go before all women gain the benefits of regular exercise.

Women in sport

Women's participation in sport lags a long way behind men's. These are some of the reasons.

Mistaken beliefs. Many sports were thought too dangerous or difficult for women. It was thought that the triple jump would leave them unable to have children, because of its high impact on the lower body. They couldn't possibly have enough strength for the pole vault.

Attitudes to women in sport. Many men, and even women, feel that sport is a man's world. It is okay for women to exercise so that they look more shapely and attractive. But being tough, competitive and muscular is not appropriate for women. How do you feel about this?

% participating in physical activity in the previous four weeks		
(excluding walking)		
Year	Male	Female
1987	57	34
1990	58	39
1993	57	39
(including walking)		
Year	Male	Female
1987	70	52
1990	73	57
1993	72	57

% of women participating in the previous four weeks		
Year	Indoor swimming	Keep fit/ yoga
1977	4	3
1980	6	2
1983	7	5
1987	11	12
1990	13	16
1993	14	17

Shortage of role models. A role model is someone you admire, and on whom you can model yourself. In the past there haven't been many role models for women in UK sport. But athletes like Sally Gunnell, Liz McColgan and Judy Simpson are helping to change this.

The media. Little coverage is given to women's sports in the media. The hidden message here is that women's sports are not important. What effect do you think this has on women's attitudes to sport?

Lack of sponsorship. Women's sports find it hard to attract sponsors. Sponsors use sport to advertise their products, and they go for the sports with most viewers. Men's sports get most viewers, and men generally have more spending power. So men's sports gets the sponsorship money.

Success in a man's world: Karren Brady, managing director of Birmingham City football club. She's the first woman to hold this position with a big professional club.

Women in other areas of sport

Sport also needs administrators, coaches and teachers. In men's sports there are very few women administrators or coaches. But even in women's sports the same is true.

Men are in control of most sports, at every level from the top down. Until 1981 the International Olympic Committee had no women members. Now 6 of the 91 members are women.

Women are perfectly able to coach other women, and to organize and run their own sports. The best way for women's sports to move forward is for women to take more responsibility for them.

The Women's Sports Foundation

This was set up in 1984. It is run by women. Its aims include these:

- to help women become involved in sport at all levels and in all areas, including coaching and managing.
- to challenge inequality in sport and bring about change.
- to improve the media coverage of women's sports.

The Foundation works closely with the Sports Council, the CCPR and other organizations to promote women's sport.

Another champion: Merlene Ottey of Jamaica. As more good female runners emerge the gap in performance between men and women is closing.

Questions

1 Describe three factors which help to explain women's low participation in physical recreation.
2 Describe two factors which help to explain its increase since the 1970s.
3 What do you think are the two *main* reasons why women's participation in sport is low?
4 If women's sports were shown on TV at weekends, just like men's, what effect would it have on:
  a participation in these sports?   b sponsorship?

5 Why don't companies who make beauty products offer more sponsorship to women's sports?
6 What is the Women's Sports Foundation?
7 In the Olympics there are no women's events in boxing, wrestling or weightlifting. Why do you think this is?
8 Are there any sports in which *you* think:
  a women should not be allowed to take part? Why?
  b the rules should be changed so that men and women can compete against each other?

15.6 Sporting behaviour?

Is bad behaviour common among athletes, or spectators, in your sport?

Sports etiquette

A sport has written rules. But it also has **etiquette** - an unwritten code of good behaviour. For example:

- a cricket player walks away from the crease when he knows he's out. He doesn't wait for the umpire to tell him.
- when a football player is injured, the ball may be kicked out of play on purpose so that the casualty can get treatment. When play resumes, it is usually given back to the team who kicked it out.

These are not *rules*. You don't have to behave this way. They are to do with a sporting attitude and a sense of fair play. What effect do you think they have among the players?

One example of tennis etiquette. Definitely not a rule of the game!

Violence among players

In some sports you hardly ever hear of athletes being rude or violent during events. Athletics, swimming and gymnastics are examples. But in other sports violence is quite common.

In June 1994, England's Jonathan Callard needed 25 stitches in his head and face after being stamped on during a rugby match against South Africa. In 1995 the Everton footballer Duncan Ferguson got a 3-month jail sentence for head-butting an opponent.

Violence among players damages a sport. It is the job of the club managers, coaches and governing bodies to curb it.

The role of spectators

You can be a spectator at home in front of the TV, or at a live venue. Either way, you are important to sport.

- At a live venue spectators help their teams by cheering them on. The atmosphere can be really exciting. Teams are more likely to win at home than away. Why do you think this is?
- They help to fund their favourite clubs by buying tickets for events, and flags, posters and other merchandise.
- Without TV spectators, sport just wouldn't get shown on TV. Without sport on TV, clubs and athletes would have far more difficulty in finding sponsorship.

Violence among spectators

As a spectator you help sport. But you can also harm it. **Football hooligans** are an example. They ruin events by fighting the opposing fans. They throw stones, bottles and other weapons on the pitch. They smash up the streets and pubs around venues.

Hooliganism is often planned in advance, even across continents. Some is linked with right-wing racist groups such as neo-Nazis. It is a problem not just for the police and clubs but for all of society.

The Heysel disaster. From the 1960s on, English hooligans gave English football a very bad reputation. The lowest point was in 1985. Liverpool were playing Juventus in the European Cup Final at the Heysel Stadium in Brussels. Liverpool fans rushed at the opposing fans. A wall collapsed and 41 Italian and Belgian fans were killed. English clubs were banned from European competitions for the next 5 years.

Combating football hooliganism

These are some of the steps taken to fight hooliganism:

- crowd segregation and fences at venues to keep rival fans apart.
- closed-circuit TV cameras around venues.
- membership schemes to make it easier to ban troublemakers.
- a ban by some clubs on all away fans.
- police in different cities and countries sharing information about known hooligans, and passing on warnings about them.

The police play a big part in preventing hooliganism. They patrol venues, the streets around them, and the local railway stations. They can have a match cancelled if they don't have the manpower to police it. The clubs have to pay towards police costs.

Football for all the family, thanks to the improvements in safety and comfort at football grounds, and the success in controlling hooliganism.

The Taylor report and all-seater stadiums

In 1989 tragedy struck at Hillsborough in Sheffield. At the FA Cup semi-final between Liverpool and Nottingham Forest, a large number of Liverpool fans were still outside the ground as kick-off approached. The police opened a large gate to let them in. In the rush for the nearest section of terracing, many fans were crushed to death in a narrow tunnel. Others were crushed on the terrace itself, the crowd trapped by the perimeter fence. 99 people died.

A government investigation into the disaster was set up, led by Lord Chief Justice Taylor. The result was the **Taylor Report**, which recommended that perimeter fences should be removed and venues made all-seater, with no more standing on the terraces.

As a result of the report, clubs were forced to spend many thousands of pounds improving their stadiums and making their grounds safer and more welcoming for spectators. Many fans are unhappy about the changes. They feel the atmosphere has been ruined and the excitement lost. But one good result is that football is becoming a family sport, with more women and children attending matches.

Questions

1. Give two examples of sporting etiquette that are not mentioned here.
2. Cheering spectators can help their team on. Do you think they have any effect on the other team?
3. Even TV spectators help sport. Explain why.
4. What happened during the Heysel disaster?
5. Describe three steps taken to fight football hooliganism.
6. What incident led to the Taylor report?
7. What did the Taylor report recommend?

Questions on Chapter 15

1 True or false? Explain your answer.
   a If you are an amateur athlete it means you are not as good as the professionals.
   b Amateur athletes in athletics can't accept prize money.
   c Appearance money is what you get for wearing your sponsor's logo.
   d Both amateur and professional golfers can compete in an open golf tournament.
   e Open sports never offer prize money.
   f If no-one wanted to watch sport there would be no professionals.

2 According to the technical definition, is the athlete amateur or professional?
   a Gabriela Sabatini
   b Eric Cantona
   c Colin Jackson
   d Sally Gunnell
   e Tanni Grey
   f Nick Faldo

3 a Explain how Trust Funds operate in amateur athletics.
   b Rugby Union used to run Trust Funds. It stopped doing so in 1995. Why was this?

4 a Is sponsorship always in the form of money? Explain.
   b Top sports stars are paid a lot to endorse products such as sports shoes and soft drinks.
      i What does *endorse* mean?
      ii Why are companies prepared to pay them for this?
   c Give one example of product endorsement by an athlete.

5 Give reasons for this.
   a Sponsors prefer to sponsor sports events shown on TV.
   b Sponsors are more prepared to sponsor men's sport than women's.
   c An unknown young athlete will find it difficult to get sponsorship.
   d A gymnastics competition is more likely to get sponsorship than a women's rugby event.
   e A sponsor is likely to cancel a contract with an athlete who is caught doping.

6 a Name two sports sponsored by tobacco companies.
   b There is pressure on TV companies not to broadcast events sponsored by tobacco companies. Why?

7 a List everything that comes under the heading *the media*.
   b Which medium has most impact on sport? Why? Give at least two reasons to support your answer.

8 The radio provides a fair amount of sports coverage.
   a What advantages does radio have over TV? List as many as you can.
   b Now list its disadvantages compared with TV.

9 a Make a table with two columns like this:

Benefits to me of watching sport on TV	Benefits to me of playing sport myself

   b Now fill in as many benefits as you can in each column.
   c Which brings more benefits?
   d What advice would you give people who spend hours watching sport on TV?

10 Sports events can sometimes appear more exciting when shown on TV than they are in real life. Explain why.

11 These are some attitudes to women in sport. For each attitude write a paragraph to oppose it.
   a Sports like football and rugby are unsuitable for women.
   b You can't be good at sports *and* attractive.
   c Women haven't got what it takes to be good at coaching.

12 'The main reason women don't participate much in sport is that they are not interested.' Do you agree? Explain.

13 Imagine you are a Minister of Sport, with a large budget. Describe three steps you would take to improve women's participation in sport. (They can be anything you want.)

14 Some people think boys and girls should be taught PE together at secondary school. Others think they should be taught separately.
   a What are the advantages of teaching them together?
   b What are the advantages of teaching them separately?
   c On balance, which would you recommend? Why?

15 tennis   gymnastics   swimming
   rugby   volleyball   football

   a From this list choose the two sports where you think:
      i violence between participants is most likely
      ii violence between participants is least likely
      iii violence among spectators is most likely
      iv violence among spectators is least likely

   b Do you think there is a connection between violence among spectators and the nature of the sport?
   c How could you test this theory?
   d Design a project for this purpose. Describe it as fully as you can.

16 'Football causes violence.' Do you agree? Explain why.

17 You are the managing director of a football club. Describe what steps you would take:
   a to combat racism
   b to combat hooliganism
   c to attract families to watch live sport.

Things to do

Amateur versus professional in sport

The division between amateurs and professionals had its origins in the class system. **Amateurs** were gentlemen who could afford to play a sport, often full time, for pleasure. **Professionals** were lower class people who earned money from sport, often by doing something for a **wager** (bet) or by competing for prizes against others.

For example gentlemen with coaches and horses had footmen. If you were the gambling type you might choose an athletic footman, and pay him something to compete in walking races against your friends' footmen. You'd put a bet on the race.

Cricket was popular among gentlemen. In the 18th century gentlemen's cricket clubs employed some lower class cricketers who were called **players**. They were paid to look after the grounds, coach the gentlemen and play against them in matches.

As sports became more organized, tension between the amateur gentlemen and working class professionals grew. In 1866 the Amateur Athletics Club was set up by gentlemen. Working class men were excluded because it was felt manual labour gave them an advantage in strength.

In 1880 the club became the Amateur Athletics Association. It redefined an amateur as someone who gained no financial reward from a sport. The working class was allowed in.

1 a Find out more about the early professional cricketers. Write a short essay about them.
   b Find a copy of an old poster for a match between gentlemen and players. What do you notice about the way their names are listed?

2 A famous example of someone walking for a wager was Captain Barclay. In 1800 he walked 1000 miles in 1000 hours for 1000 guineas.
   Try to find out more about Captain Barclay. Who put up the money? Where did he walk?

3 Find out more about the Amateur Athletics Club. Who started it? In what sports did it compete, and where? Write a short essay about it.

Sponsorship

a Make a table with these headings:

Sport	Team or individual	Sponsor	Nature of sponsor's business

b Now fill it in for as many sports and sponsors as you can.
c Look at the last column for each sport. Can you see any relationship between the sponsor's business and the sport? If yes, explain it.

Media coverage of sport

1 The work in this activity should be shared among the class.
   a Six people each collect one newspaper a day for a week (Monday to Saturday). The papers should be a mixture of **tabloids** and **broadsheets** (quality papers). One person collects the Guardian, another the Sun and so on.
   b For each newspaper make a table like the one started here:

Name of newspaper: The Independent		
Sport	Type	Number of articles
Football	Men's	JHT III
	Women's	I
Rugby	Men's	III
	Women's	

   c Go through all the sport pages in your set of papers. (A new person can take over for each copy.) For each article on sport, put a tally mark in the table.
   d Now add up the tally marks for each sport. Put the results in a table like this:

Total number of articles in the Independent for the week		
Sport	Men's	Women's
Football	54	
Rugby		

   e Show the results as a bar chart. Put the women's sports at one end of the chart and the men's at the other. Put each in order, the sport with most coverage first.
   f Study the bar chart. Which sports get most coverage? Which get least? How well are women's sports covered? Write a report on what you have discovered.

2 Now compare the bar graphs for the different papers.
   a Do the same sports get most coverage in all of them? Which sports are these?
   b Is it true that the quality press provides more coverage of minority sports?
   c Which paper covers most women's sports?
   d Overall, how does coverage of women's sports compare with that of men's? Try to express it as a percentage.

3 Now pick the main sports event of the week. Compare coverage of this event in a quality paper and a tabloid.
   a What differences do you notice?
   b Do you agree with the statements in the table on page 181?

4 Your task is to compare weekend sports coverage for the BBC and BSkyB. You will need TV listings for Saturday and Sunday. For these two days count:
   a how many hours of sport each organization puts out
   b how many different sports each covers
   Write a report on what you have found.

189

Index

Bold entries show where a term is defined or explained.